BUFFALO BILL

By FRANK LEE BEALS

EMMETT A. BETTS, *Editor*

Research Professor, School of Education
University of Miami
Coral Gables, Florida

Illustrations by
JACK MERRYWEATHER

ROW, PETERSON AND COMPANY

Evanston, Illinois   Elmsford, New York

★

THE AMERICAN ADVENTURE SERIES

★

1962

Table of Contents

A Man's Job

The Young Trappers

Boys of the Pony

Wagon Trains, Stagecoaches, and Railroads

Buffalo Bill, Army Scout

THE STORY of the winning of the West is one of the most thrilling chapters in the history of our country.

It is a story of the plains, filled with the courageous deeds of gallant men and women.

One of the colorful figures among those who helped push our civilization westward over the plains was William Frederick Cody, better known and loved as Buffalo Bill.

This story of his adventurous life was written to give young Americans some idea of how much they owe to those who helped lay the foundations of this great country of ours. It is also hoped that it will serve to keep alive the name and fame of the last of the great scouts.

FRANK LEE BEALS
EMMETT A. BETTS

Billy Cody's First Job

YOUNG Billy Cody pulled his galloping horse to a stop in front of a large building. Painted in black letters across the front of the building was the sign:

LEAVENWORTH, KANSAS
GATEWAY TO THE WEST
RUSSELL, MAJORS & WADDELL
WAGON TRAINS   SUPPLIES

Billy dismounted and tied his horse to a post. He hurried into the building. He went straight to the office of Alec Majors who was a partner in the firm of Russell, Majors & Waddell.

"Uncle Alec," said Billy, "I want to go West with your next wagon train. Will you give me a job?"

"I will find something for you to do," answered Alec Majors. "But I am afraid that I can't give

1

you a job with one of our wagon trains."

"I don't want just 'something to do,' " broke in Billy. "I want a job—a real job. I want to work with a wagon train."

"You are too young, Billy."

"I am almost twelve years old," said Billy. "I can ride and shoot as well as a man. And besides, Uncle Alec, I must have a job."

"Does your mother know that you want to go West with a wagon train?" asked Alec Majors.

"Yes, sir," answered Billy. "Now that my father is dead, I am the man of the family. I want to take care of my mother and sisters."

"Of course you do, Billy, and I want to help you," smiled Alec Majors. "But you are asking for a man's job with a wagon train."

At this time there were no railroads west of the Mississippi River. All the freight that was shipped overland to the Pacific coast had to be hauled by wagon train.

The firm of Russell, Majors & Waddell owned and operated a large overland freight business. More than six thousand of its freight wagons traveled the Western trails. The firm employed over eight thousand men. It owned seventy-five thousand head of oxen which were used to pull the heavy wagons. It also owned thousands of cattle, mules, and horses.

From early spring until late fall, the firm's wagon trains moved back and forth over a two-thousand-mile trail which led across the great plains and mountains. The wagon trains carried food and supplies to the early settlers in the far West. Most of the wagons, however, hauled large quantities of freight to the United States soldiers stationed on the plains to protect the Western pioneers.

Alec Majors hired all the men who worked for the firm. Years before, he had hauled freight across the prairies and mountains. He knew from experience the many hardships and dangers of such a job. He asked men to do only the things that he himself was willing to do. He was stern, but kindly. He was a very religious man. He was just and fair. He was well known and respected by everyone who knew him. Billy, like most of the boys in Leavenworth, called him Uncle Alec.

"Billy," continued Alec Majors, "I am afraid that a job with a wagon train is too dangerous for a boy twelve years old."

"I know it is a dangerous job," said Billy, "but I can take care of myself."

"Think of the Indians, Billy. You never know where they may be lying in wait for a chance to send an arrow or a bullet into you."

"I am not afraid of Indians," said Billy.

"But do you know about the danger from buffalo stampedes? A herd of buffalo on stampede can wreck a wagon train or wipe out a whole camp in a few minutes."

"I know," answered Billy. "I have heard your scouts tell about buffalo stampedes on the plains. I am not afraid, Uncle Alec."

Alec Majors smiled. "All right, Billy," he said, "but what about outlaws? They are as dangerous as the Indians."

"I know," was Billy's answer.

"There are other dangers, too, Billy. Life on the plains is hard. There may be times when you will have no water and but little food. Thirst and hunger are hard to endure, even for an old plainsman, Billy. The trails are long and dusty. The rivers and streams are without bridges. They must be forded. Sometimes teams and wagons get stuck in the sand or in the mud and everyone has to help pull them out."

"I know there are dangers and hardships on the plains, but I am not afraid," said Billy. "Please, Uncle Alec, give me a job with a wagon train."

Alec Majors leaned over his desk. He studied the eager face of the boy standing before him.

Billy was tall for his age. He was slender and he held himself proudly erect. He was dressed in buckskin clothes. His eyes were brown and his golden, curly hair fell to his straight shoulders. He was a handsome boy and, in spite of his youth, there was an air of self-confidence about him.

"Very well, Billy. I will give you a job with one of the wagon trains leaving for the West. Your job will be riding cavayard. You know what that means, don't you?"

"Oh, yes. Riding cavayard is herding all the

extra cattle and horses that go with the wagon
train. If they are allowed to stray they will get
lost, or they will be stolen by the Indians. Riding
cavayard is an important job."

"Yes, it is an important job, Billy. Your pay
will be the same as that of other men who ride
cavayard, forty dollars a month and your food."

"Thank you, Uncle Alec. I —"

As Billy was speaking, the door of the office was
thrown open. A scout rushed into the room. His
buckskin clothes were torn and stained with blood.

Majors jumped to his feet. "What's happened?
What are you doing here?" he questioned. "By
this time your wagon train should be somewhere
along the Platte River."

"Indians!" exclaimed the scout. "Surprise attack—no chance to defend ourselves—all the men
were killed—wagons burned—animals driven off.
Our outfit was completely wiped out."

"This is terrible news," said Majors as he dropped back into his chair. "Some of our best men
were with that outfit. We can replace the animals
and wagons, but we cannot replace such men."

"We put up a good fight," said the scout.

"I'm sure you did. Well, in spite of this terrible loss, we must keep the freight moving. Get some rest and take care of yourself. Can you be ready to go out again in a few days?"

"Yes, Mr. Majors, I'll be ready. All I need now is some rest," said the scout as he left the office.

Majors turned to Billy and asked, "Do you still want a job with one of our wagon trains, Billy?"

"Yes, I do," answered Billy.

"All right, but before you can work for our firm you have to sign an oath. Every man who works for Russell, Majors & Waddell must take this oath. I will read it to you:

"I, William Frederick Cody, do hereby swear before the great and living God: that while I am in the employ of Russell, Majors & Waddell, I will not use profane language; that I will not quarrel with any other employee of the firm; that I will not abuse nor neglect the animals; and, that I will conduct myself honestly. I will be faithful to my duties, and will act at all times so as to win the confidence of my employers. So help me God."

"I will sign the oath," said Billy, "and I shall do my very best to live up to it."

"Here is a Bible I want you to keep, Billy," said Majors. "I give a Bible to each man when he signs the oath and starts to work for our firm."

"Thank you, Uncle Alec. I am glad to have a Bible of my own."

"Now report to Frank McCarthy. He is one of the best wagon bosses in the West. His wagon train pulls out tomorrow. If you can get him to accept you as a cavayard rider with his train, you may go with him. I know how well you can ride, but you may have to prove it to McCarthy. He is boss of his train. If he doesn't want you to go with him, you will have to wait and go out with some other wagon train."

Billy hurried out to find Frank McCarthy. He found him in the wagon yard helping repair a covered wagon.

"Mr. McCarthy," said Billy. "I am Billy Cody. Uncle Alec Majors told me to report to you."

"And what is it you want with me, lad?" asked McCarthy.

"I should like to go with your wagon train, Mr. McCarthy," answered Billy eagerly.

McCarthy threw back his head and laughed. "And what can a boy like you do with my wagon train?"

"I want to ride cavayard."

"Ride cavayard! Can you ride a bucking horse?"

Without waiting for Billy's answer, McCarthy called to one of his men, "Saddle Prince and bring him here."

In a short time a prancing horse was led to where McCarthy and Billy were standing. The horse reared and struck out with his forefeet.

"Do you want to change your mind, lad?" asked McCarthy.

"No, I will ride him," answered Billy.

Prince was a fine looking animal. His broad chest and clean-cut legs were signs that he had speed and strength. His well-shaped head and neck meant a fine spirit. The only mark on his brown body was a white star on his forehead.

Billy held out his hand and the horse jerked his head away.

"This horse has been abused," said Billy.

"Yes, he has," said McCarthy, "and when I found it out I fired the man who was abusing him. No one who abuses animals can work for this firm or with my wagon train."

Billy patted Prince on the neck. When Prince had quieted down, Billy adjusted the stirrup straps to the right length. He allowed an arm's length for each strap. He patted Prince again and then quickly swung himself into the saddle.

Instantly Prince's head went down and up went his back. He bucked, and turned, and twisted. But Billy sat firmly in the saddle.

McCarthy was tense as he watched the struggle between Billy and this wild Western horse. His large, rough hands gripped the rim of the wagon wheel. It took the skill of a real horseman to ride Prince.

Suddenly Prince stopped bucking and like a flash of lightning struck out across the prairie. Billy swayed gracefully in the saddle.

"Watch that boy ride!" shouted McCarthy as he threw his hat into the air.

Billy let the horse run without trying to bring him to a stop. After about a mile of hard galloping, the horse began to slow down. Billy pulled him about and headed back toward McCarthy.

"You win, lad," said McCarthy as Billy rode up to him. "You have a job with my wagon train and you may have the horse, too."

"Do you mean that I may have Prince for my own?" asked Billy as he swung to the ground.

"He's yours," said McCarthy. "Prince is a spirited horse, but you have shown me that you can handle him. You need a good horse when you are riding the plains. Does that horse over there in front of Majors' office belong to you?"

"It belongs to my mother."

"Take Prince home with you. You can lead the other horse. Leave your mother's horse at home for her to use while you are away. Don't forget, Billy, my train pulls out early tomorrow morning. Be ready if you are to ride with me."

"I'll be ready," promised Billy.

Billy Cody's life of adventure on the plains of the West was about to begin.

Westward Ho!

THAT NIGHT as Billy ate his supper his mother said, "Billy, you are too young to have so much responsibility. I think it would be better to move back East and live with my family. Your sisters are enjoying their visit in the East and I am sure that you would like to live there, too."

"No, Mother," protested Billy. "Our home is in the West. We belong here. You promised me that I would have this chance to prove that I can take care of you and my sisters."

"I know, Billy." Mrs. Cody smiled gently. "But I shall worry about you."

"Don't worry about me, Mother. I will be with Frank McCarthy. He is one of the best wagon bosses in the West. He has given me a wonderful horse to ride. Besides, Uncle Alec is paying me forty dollars a month and I have asked him to give the money to you each month. He said that if I needed any money, I could get some from Frank McCarthy."

"Oh, Billy, I did promise you that you could have this chance and if ever a mother was proud of her son, I am proud of you."

Early the next morning Billy kissed his mother good-by. He mounted Prince and started to town where he was to join McCarthy's wagon train. When he reached the top of the hill he turned in his saddle and looked back. His mother was still standing in the doorway of the cabin.

"Good-by, Mother," he called.

"Good-by, Billy," came her answer. "Be careful and hurry back home to me."

Billy touched Prince lightly and galloped on to Leavenworth. As soon as he arrived he reported to McCarthy.

"Good morning, Billy," called McCarthy. Then he turned and called to a young man riding by, "Hi there, Bob, here is the boy who signed up to ride with you and your men. His name is Billy Cody. Take him with you and show him what he has to do."

"Thank you, Mr. McCarthy," said Billy as he went to join Bob. But McCarthy did not heed the boy's reply. He was again busy inspecting the wagons and teams of oxen, and giving final orders to his men. He was everywhere at once. Nothing escaped his quick eye. Without question McCarthy was boss of his wagon train. His word was law and his men obeyed him promptly and willingly.

McCarthy was a man of the plains. He was tall and powerful. He wore buckskin clothes and a large, white felt hat. His face was tanned by the wind and sun. His movements were quick and noiseless. His blue, Irish eyes were keen and clear. There was an easy air of command and leadership in his bold manner. He was rough, but he was generous and kind and a loyal friend.

McCarthy's wagon train was made up of thirty-five wagons. Each wagon was pulled by three yoke (pairs) of oxen. Oxen were used because they could stand the long, hard trip of two thousand miles far better than horses or mules. Oxen could make the entire trip, but horses or mules had to be changed at relay stations along the trail.

The wagons were strong and especially built for travel over the rough plains and mountain trails. They were turned up at the ends like boats and were watertight. They were built this way to protect the supplies when crossing the rivers and streams which had to be forded. Their shape also kept the heavy loads from sliding back and forth as the wagons were pulled up or down hill.

The wagons were usually called covered wagons because they were covered with heavy canvas. The canvas was stretched over rounded hoops to form a top for the wagon. The canvas protected the supplies from rain and dust. Sometimes the wagons were called prairie schooners because of their boat-like shape.

On this trip, McCarthy's train was carrying a valuable load of food and military supplies for the soldiers stationed in Utah. In addition, a thousand head of cattle were to be driven over the plains along with the train. They were to furnish beef for the soldiers.

McCarthy soon finished his inspection and his train was ready to start on its long trip westward.

The drivers of the wagons took their places on the high front seats. Mounted men, armed with rifles, moved to their positions beside the wagons.

"Stretch out!" shouted McCarthy.

The driver of the first wagon held up a long bull whip. He snapped the whip out over the heads of his oxen. The whip cracked like a pistol shot. The oxen leaned forward in their yokes and slowly the wagon began to move. Then, one by one, other drivers cracked their whips and, one by one, the

wagons rolled over the streets of Leavenworth and headed for the Western trail over the plains.

The cattle, herded by Billy and the other cava-yard riders, followed behind the last wagon.

"Billy," said Bob as they rode along, "our job is to herd the cattle and to deliver them in good condition at the end of the trip. But that is not all McCarthy expects us to do. He expects every man with his train to keep his eyes and ears open. 'Be alert!' is McCarthy's motto. That is why he is one of the best wagon bosses in the West."

"I am glad to be with him on my first trip with a wagon train," said Billy.

"I am surprised that McCarthy agreed to take you," laughed Bob. "Several times he has refused to take cavayard riders who have had no experience on the plains. What did you do to him to make him change his mind?"

"I guess it was because I rode Prince for him," answered Billy as he patted his horse. "Mr. McCarthy gave him to me. Prince is a wonderful horse."

"You like horses, don't you?"

"Oh, yes," answered Billy. "My father always had good horses and he taught me to ride when I was four years old."

"Was your father Isaac Cody, the man who owned an Indian trading post near Leavenworth?"

"Yes," answered Billy, "and many of the Indians are my friends. I have often gone to their camps. I know some of them very well. I learned to speak their language."

Bob shook his head. "Too bad you didn't learn the sign language. If you had, then you could talk to any Indian, even if you didn't know how to speak the language of his tribe."

"But I did learn many of the signs that the Indians use," broke in Billy.

"Look out, Billy. Ride to the left!" called Bob. "The cattle are trying to break for the open plain."

The cavayard riders kept the cattle moving. The men had to watch the herd closely to prevent them from straying from the trail. Billy and Bob rode together on one side of the herd.

At the end of the first day, McCarthy ordered a halt. The drivers pulled their wagons into position forming a circle. In case of attack this made a fort for defense. The oxen were turned out to graze.

The chuck wagon, with a cook in charge, was in the center of the circle. Campfires were made and the cook began to prepare the evening meal.

"Bob," ordered McCarthy, "post your men for two-hour guard duty. Send Billy to me. He won't need to stand guard tonight."

When Billy had taken care of Prince he joined the men gathered around a big campfire.

"Well, Billy," asked McCarthy, "how did you get along today?"

"I got along all right, Mr. McCarthy. Bob told me that you said I did not need to stand guard tonight. But I want to do my part. I want to do everything the other men do. If they stand guard, I want to stand guard, too."

"That's the spirit, Billy. After supper report back to Bob and he will give you your orders. We don't expect any trouble, but you never can tell."

As the men waited for supper they laughed and talked. They joked with Billy.

"Did you join us to share our exciting life?" questioned a driver.

"That was one reason," answered Billy, "but perhaps my best reason is that I want to take care of my mother and sisters. You see my father is dead. I am now the man of my family. I am going to try to do a man's work with this wagon train."

For a minute the men were silent. Then they cheered, "Hurrah for Billy Cody!"

Billy's quiet, determined spirit won their hearts. They were his friends and McCarthy was pleased.

A few hours later, Billy was standing guard with Bob.

"Billy," said Bob, "I know that you will make good on this trip. You have already shown that you are willing to do your part. McCarthy is not a hard man to work for, but he demands that each man do his share of the work. McCarthy will be your friend and, Billy, you couldn't have a better friend."

Early in the morning a bugle sounded. The camp came to life. The cook quickly prepared breakfast for the scouts who left before the wagons moved out of camp. Then the men of the first wagon section ate their breakfast and hurried to get their oxen yoked for the day's trip. Other sections followed in turn. A short time after sunrise the wagon train was on its way over the trail.

The wagon train made good time on its trip westward. It covered from twelve to fifteen miles a day.

Each night Billy took his turn on guard duty with Bob. They were always together and soon became good friends.

Billy was a favorite with the men of the wagon train. He was always busy and happy and he never complained. At night when the day's work was over and the men had gathered around the campfire, Billy was usually with them. He joined the men as they sang the old plains song "Mustang Gray."

> There was a noble stranger,
> They called him Mustang Gray;
> He left his home when but a youth,
> Went ranging far away.

> Chorus: But he'll go no more a-ranging
> The savage to affright;
> For he's heard his last war whoop
> And has fought his last fight.

Almost every day the wagon train met stage-coaches and other wagon trains returning to Leavenworth from the west. The drivers and scouts of the trains reported to McCarthy that they had not met any Indians on the trail.

After several weeks, McCarthy's wagon train

was rolling over the dusty trail in western Nebraska. One day at noon, McCarthy ordered a halt for the noonday meal and rest period. As usual, the drivers formed their wagons in a circle and, as usual, the men gathered around the chuck wagon. Two men remained outside the circle, guarding the cattle.

The train had stopped on a high bluff overlooking the Platte River about thirty-five miles west of Fort Kearney. The banks of the river, in some places, were thirty feet high.

It was a hot summer day. The men and animals were tired. Most of the men after eating their noonday meal, crawled under the wagons and went to sleep.

"Well, Billy," said Bob, "it's our turn to stand guard."

Billy jumped to his feet and started for Prince.

Suddenly from outside the circle two rifle shots rang out. A wild, piercing war whoop filled the air. The two guards, whose places Billy and Bob were to have taken, fell dead.

"Indians!" shouted McCarthy.

Instantly the men ran for their rifles.

There was a thunder of pounding hoofs. A yelling band of Indians came racing toward the camp.

McCarthy's men returned their fire and the Indians retreated. But in a short time the Indians swept down upon them again—and again! Several men fell wounded beside their wagons. The cattle and oxen stampeded.

"Get over the bluff, men!" shouted McCarthy. "We are outnumbered! We can't save the wagon train, but we can try to save our lives. Billy, you stay with me."

McCarthy and his men, carrying their wounded, made for the river bluff. The Indians closed in on the wagons. They broke open boxes and cases. They threw out everything.

"Men," said McCarthy, "this is our chance to escape. The Indians are too busy destroying our supplies to follow us for a while. We must try to get back to Fort Kearney."

"There goes an Indian with Prince," called Billy.

"Too bad, son, but there is nothing we can do about it."

"Look at my chuck wagon," shouted the cook. "They are tearing it apart. There goes an Indian with my pots and pans. I'll stop him."

The cook took careful aim and fired. The Indian threw up his arms and fell forward. Pots and pans went in every direction.

"Stop that!" ordered McCarthy. "Do you want them to get our scalps? Now get going! Stay behind the bank of the river! Keep together! When those Indians have finished looting the wagons they will begin looking for us."

McCarthy and his men edged their way along the river bank. At times they were forced to wade in deep water. At other times they crawled along under the steep banks. It was hard work carrying the wounded men, but they struggled on. They were tired, but they did not stop. Darkness fell and the men slowly made their way through the night. The moon rose and the trees along the river bank cast shadows on the water.

It was difficult for Billy to keep up with the men. The water was deep and he had to wade holding his rifle above his head. His rifle and ammunition were heavy. Gradually he fell behind. He stopped for a moment to rest. He looked up at the moon.

An Indian war bonnet appeared over the bluff. Slowly the rising figure of a warrior was outlined against the moonlight. The warrior pulled back his bow ready to shoot an arrow in the direction of McCarthy's men. Billy raised his rifle to his shoulder and squeezed the trigger.

The crack of the rifle stopped McCarthy and his men in their tracks.

"Who fired that shot?" called McCarthy.

"Someone behind us," answered Bob.

"Who's there?" shouted McCarthy.

"Billy Cody," came the reply.

"Stay where you are. I'm coming back," called McCarthy. When he reached Billy he asked, "What happened?"

"I shot at an Indian who was following us."

McCarthy slipped down the bank. "You've killed an Indian all right, Billy. You saved the life of at least one of us. Give me your rifle. I'll carry it."

"Mr. McCarthy, were those Sioux Indians?" asked Billy.

"No, they were Cheyennes. There is one Cheyenne chief I like to avoid."

"What's his name?" asked Billy.

"Chief Yellow Hand," answered McCarthy. "I
expect trouble from him every time he crosses my
trail."

All night McCarthy and his men pushed on.

As day dawned they reached Fort Kearney. The
soldiers gave them food and places to sleep. They
rested while a troop of cavalry went back to look
for the wagon train.

Later in the day Billy asked McCarthy, "Do you
think Yellow Hand had anything to do with the
attack on our wagon train?"

"Yes, I believe he did."

"Then he or one of his Indians stole Prince.
Someday I intend to get Prince back. Yellow
Hand may be a Cheyenne chief, but he can't have
my horse."

"The Indians like horses, so they will be good
to him. Maybe you'll get him back someday. But
don't forget, Billy, you're lucky to be alive."

On to Fort Laramie

THE SOLDIERS returned to the fort and reported that the Indians had burned the wagon train and driven off the cattle. McCarthy decided to return to Leavenworth with his men. Billy's first trip had ended in disaster. But he had won the friendship and respect of the men with whom he worked. They liked his determination to share the work and the dangers of the trip.

When they reached Leavenworth, they told how Billy had killed an Indian warrior and saved the life of at least one of the men. They told how he had marched all night without a word of complaint.

Billy was praised by Alec Majors and other oldtimers of the plains. Mrs. Cody was proud of her son. The boys of Leavenworth envied him and looked upon him as a hero.

A few days after their return, McCarthy said to Billy, "Alec Majors tells me that Lew Simpson is ready to leave with his wagon train. I want you to go West with him."

"But Mr. McCarthy," interrupted Billy, "I want to go with you when your train is ready."

"It will be several weeks before I can get another wagon train ready to leave, and you need a job, Billy. Lew Simpson is a good wagon boss. He is my friend and I've told him about you. He needs another cavayard rider. The job is yours if you want it. He is headed for Fort Laramie."

"Fort Laramie!" exclaimed Billy. "Why, that is where all the famous scouts and trappers meet. I might even see Kit Carson there."

McCarthy nodded. "That's true, Billy. And don't forget that Fort Laramie is in the center of the Indian country. Bob has already signed up to ride with Simpson. Don't you want to go, too?"

"Oh, yes, Mr. McCarthy," answered Billy, "but I will be sorry not to be with you."

"Don't worry about that, Billy. You and I will have many trips together. Now come with me and I'll take you to your new wagon boss."

When they found the wagon boss, McCarthy

said, "Simpson, here's the lad I told you about."

"Hello, Billy Cody," smiled Simpson. "I am glad to have you with my train. Report to Bob. He is in charge of the cavayard riders. We leave early tomorrow morning."

"Thank you, Mr. Simpson. I'll be ready."

The trip to Fort Laramie was long and difficult. Simpson, like McCarthy, was a fearless, but cautious wagon boss. Daily his scouts rode far ahead of the wagon train. At night guards were posted to keep close watch on the camp and animals. Day by day, the heavy wagons rumbled on over the dusty trail. Now and then, scattered bands of Indian braves were sighted, but they did not attack the train. Weeks later, the wagon train neared the fort.

Fort Laramie was built on a bluff overlooking the Laramie River. It was a square fort about the size of half a city block. It was made of adobe (sun-dried brick) with walls twenty feet high and four feet thick.

In 1834, a fur trading company had built the adobe buildings to be used as a trading post. Some ten years later the United States government bought the post and then it became an important military fort as well as a trading post. It was a famous meeting place for scouts, trappers, Indians, and the men of the wagon trains.

The wagon trains of Russell, Majors & Waddell traveling over the Oregon Trail always stopped at Fort Laramie. Here the firm operated a supply station for its men. There was a blacksmith shop and a large warehouse stored with food, clothing, ammunition, and other supplies. There were corrals for oxen, cattle, horses, and mules. After a long, difficult overland trip, the men looked forward to a few days of rest at Fort Laramie.

Slowly Simpson's wagon train rolled on. Clouds of dust, kicked up by the animals and wagons, hung over the trail. At last the outline of the fort appeared in the distance. Near the fort several thousand Indians were camped. Their tepees and campfires were strung out along the river bank for miles. Back from the river and outside the walls of the fort were corrals and camping spaces for wagon trains.

Simpson, mounted on his horse, was in the lead. He turned in his saddle and, waving his hand toward a camping space, called to the driver of the first wagon, "Ride in!" He gave his horse the spurs and raced on ahead of the train.

The order was called from wagon to wagon. Bull whips cracked and the oxen broke into a run. The wagons rattled and bounced over the rough ground.

Billy, Bob, and the other cavayard riders guided the herd of cattle to a corral. When the cattle were corraled, the riders cared for their horses. It was late when they joined the men of the wagon train who had already made camp near the fort. Supper was ready and Billy ate hurriedly.

"Why are you in such a rush?" asked Bob.

"I am going to the fort," answered Billy.

"The fort will be there tomorrow," laughed one of the men. "You had better rest in camp tonight."

As the man said this, a voice called from the direction of the fort, "Billy Cody, come here."

Billy jumped to his feet and ran toward the fort.

Simpson was waiting for him near the main gate.

"Come with me, Billy. I have a surprise for you," smiled Simpson.

"What is it?" questioned Billy.

"It wouldn't be a surprise if I told you."

"Have you found Prince?"

"No," laughed Simpson.

Billy followed Simpson through the big gate of the fort and into a large open square. They made their way across the square to a big building. They entered a room where a group of officers and men were laughing and talking.

Standing in the center of the group was a slim man dressed in deerskin and Indian moccasins. He was speaking. His voice was gentle and low. But there was something in his quiet manner that held Billy's attention. There was something in the man's keen, blue eyes and in his proud, but modest, bearing which Billy admired.

"Who is that man?" he whispered.

Simpson threw back his head and roared with laughter. "I knew it, Billy," he said. "I knew that would be your first question."

Simpson signaled to the man.

The man nodded and strode across the room. His movements were quick and noiseless.

"Billy," said Simpson, "I want you to meet Kit Carson."

"Kit Carson!" exclaimed Billy.

The famous scout held out his hand. "Billy," he smiled, "Simpson tells me that you are doing a man's job for him. You are younger than I thought you would be. What do you like best about working with a wagon train?"

Billy tried to answer but could not speak.

Ever since the beginning of this trip, Billy had looked forward to the chance of meeting Kit Carson at Fort Laramie. On many nights, Billy had fallen asleep under a wagon planning the questions he would ask the famous scout. "What does a boy have to learn in order to be a scout?" "What does he need to know about Indians?" He had thought of these and countless other questions. And now, here was Kit Carson smiling down at him! He could not speak.

Kit put his hand on Billy's shoulder and began to talk to Simpson. The two men were old friends.

They talked about the plains, Indians, wagon trains, new settlers, and friends in the West. Now and then, Kit explained some point to Billy. Almost before Billy realized it he was laughing and talking as though he had known Kit a long time.

Finally Billy said, "I want to be a scout when I grow up, Mr. Carson, and I want to be a good scout like you."

"I am glad to hear you say that, Billy," smiled Kit. "I am proud to be a scout because I am doing my part to help build the West. If you really want to become a scout, learn all you can about the Indians. Learn their languages, their habits, and their customs, as well as how to follow a trail and how to look for signs. Make friends with the Indians, for if you are a true friend they will trust you."

"My father had an Indian trading post," replied Billy, "and I used to play with the Indian boys when they came to the post."

"Did you learn to speak their language?" asked Kit.

"Yes," answered Billy, "and I also learned some

of the signs used in the sign language."

"Good!" exclaimed Kit. "I use the sign language most of the time. I know the languages of many tribes, but I can talk to any Indian by means of the sign language."

"I learned some of the signs because I thought it was fun," said Billy. "Now, I shall try to learn as many more signs as I can. While we are here at Fort Laramie, I will make friends with the Indians camped near the fort."

"I would do that, Billy, if I were you." Then turning to Simpson, Kit asked, "How long will your wagon train be here?"

"A part of my train will be here two months— maybe three," answered Simpson. "Some of my men will be delivering supplies to the new fort being built about fifty miles from here. Fifteen of my wagons are loaded with supplies for Fort Bridger. I am leaving for Fort Bridger in a few days with the men who are driving these wagons."

"Are you taking Billy with you?"

"No, he is to stay here at Fort Laramie. When I get back I am going to organize two large wagon trains for our return trip to Leavenworth."

"Tomorrow I am riding to an Indian camp some distance from the fort," said Kit. "I had planned to go alone, but maybe Billy would like to go with me. If he wants to be a scout, he should know all he can about as many different Indian tribes as possible."

"I would like to go with you, Mr. Carson," broke in Billy, "but I have to help unload our wagons."

"You may go with Kit," said Simpson. "I will have Bob do your work."

"Oh, thank you, Mr. Simpson," said Billy. He added quickly, "I will do extra guard duty for Bob when I return."

"Then it is settled, Billy," smiled Kit. "Meet me at the gates of the fort tomorrow morning at five o'clock."

"I'll be waiting," promised Billy.

Chief Yellow Hand

EARLY in the morning, Billy and Kit were on their way to the Indian camp. They rode southward across the prairie. Their horses were swift, but neither Kit nor Billy rode his horse at a hard gallop. They kept the horses at a steady, even pace of about ten miles an hour. They let the horses rest every three or four hours.

While they were resting their horses and eating their noonday meal, Kit said, "Billy, I have been watching the way you handle a horse. You ride like a Plains Indian. And there is no better horseman than a Plains Indian. You ought to have a good horse of your own."

"I had a good horse," said Billy. "His name was Prince. He was stolen by the Indians when they burned Mr. McCarthy's wagon train. I was riding cavayard for Mr. McCarthy. But I intend to get Prince back someday."

"Do you know which tribe of Indians burned the wagons and stole Prince?"

"Yes, Yellow Hand and his Cheyenne braves."

"You may get Prince back sooner than you expected," laughed Kit. "We are on our way to Yellow Hand's camp."

"Yellow Hand's camp!" exclaimed Billy. "Then I will get Prince and ride him back to the fort."

Kit shook his head. "Not so fast, Billy. You can't just ride into Yellow Hand's camp and pick out your horse and ride away. You must have a better plan than that.

"The commanding officer at Fort Laramie has given me a special order to carry out, Billy. If I can carry out his order successfully I may be able to get Prince, too. But first we must be certain that Prince is in Yellow Hand's camp. I will need your help."

"How can I help you?" asked Billy eagerly.

"I want you to forget about Prince for a while," answered Kit. "You may see him in the Indian camp. If you do, you are to do nothing that will let Yellow Hand know that Prince is your horse."

"I shall do as you say," said Billy.

"If I weren't sure of that," smiled Kit, "I would send you back to the fort right now."

After a few moments Kit continued, "Billy, during the last month, two hundred horses have been stolen from the wagon trains in this section. Alec Majors reported this loss to the commanding officer at Fort Laramie. The officer sent for me and asked me to find the horses. I located them in Yellow Hand's camp.

"When I reported this to the officer, he was determined to send soldiers to take the horses by force. But I asked him to let me go to Yellow Hand and try to get the horses back without the use of the troops."

Kit laughed as he added, "I hope I don't have to talk to Yellow Hand as long as I had to talk to the officer to get my own way."

They finished their meal and started for their horses.

"What will you say to Yellow Hand?" asked Billy.

Kit called back over his shoulder, "I am going to

tell him to return two hundred and one horses to Fort Laramie."

"Two hundred and one!" exclaimed Billy. "You mean that you will get Prince back for me?"

"If Prince is in Yellow Hand's camp, he will be returned with the other horses. Come, let's ride."

They mounted their horses and rode on.

"Billy," said Kit, "you will need a sign to let me know if you see Prince. When I ask you if you like Yellow Hand's camp, answer yes if you have seen Prince. If you have not seen Prince, pretend that you did not hear me. If your answer is yes, I shall then ask you which brave you think is the finest warrior in the camp. You will point out the brave who has your horse. That is all, Billy. Say nothing more."

Late that afternoon, Kit and Billy reached Yellow Hand's camp. The squaws, cooking the evening meal over the campfires, looked up as Kit and Billy rode to the square in the center of the camp. In the square, laughing children were playing and a few old braves were sitting in a circle smoking their pipes.

Billy followed Kit as he rode to the largest tepee facing the square. An old brave standing by the tepee came forward. Kit reined in his horse and dismounted. "I wish to see your chief," he said.

"Yellow Hand and braves hunt today," answered the old brave.

"When come back to camp?"

"Sundown," answered the brave.

"We wait for Yellow Hand," said Kit.

An hour later the hunting party returned. Shouting and singing, the braves raced their horses into the square.

"Here comes Yellow Hand," said Kit, as the chief, mounted on a beautiful horse, rode into the square. Yellow Hand was riding Prince!

"Prince," said Billy to himself, "I have found you." But not a sign of excitement nor surprise betrayed Billy's happiness. Not a sign!

Yellow Hand dismounted. Turning to the old brave who stood near, he commanded, "Take care of Swift Eagle." Then proudly he strode toward his tepee where Kit and Billy were waiting.

Yellow Hand was a tall, handsome chief. He was

wearing a war bonnet of eagle feathers which hung down his back and almost touched the ground. His fringed doeskin trousers were as soft as velvet. Beaded bands circled the powerful muscles of his upper arms. He held himself straight as an arrow.

"Friend," he said to Kit, "Yellow Hand welcomes you and white boy. Stay with my people tonight. We dance for you."

"We cannot stay," replied Kit. "We must return to Fort Laramie."

"My braves ride with you until the moon is up."

"No, thank you," smiled Kit. "I shall see you at the fort in a few days."

"I have no reason to come to white man's fort. My people have supplies."

"Yellow Hand," said Kit, "you have not been to the fort for many months. If your people are well-supplied, that means only one thing. You have taken the supplies from the white man's wagon trains. But I did not come here to talk to you about supplies. I came to talk with you because your braves have been taking the white man's horses. You may keep the supplies, but the horses must be returned to Fort Laramie in five days."

"We keep white man's horses," began Yellow Hand. "White man shoot our buffalo, take our land, and kill our people. You have always been our friend. Why have you changed? You talk like white war chief."

"I am your friend and you know it," answered Kit. "The white war chief was ready to march to your camp. But I asked—"

"Let him come," broke in Yellow Hand. "My braves are not afraid to fight."

"Do not speak to me in anger when I am trying to be a friend to you and your people," said Kit.

Kit's low, gentle voice suddenly became sharp and firm. Billy had been watching Prince, but now he looked up quickly.

"Yellow Hand," continued Kit, "you have two hundred horses belonging to the white man. They are to be returned. I will give you exactly five days to bring them back to Fort Laramie. If they are not returned by the end of five days, the soldiers will march to your camp and I will come with them."

"You would not march against my people," said Yellow Hand. "You are trying to bluff me."

"Did I ever tell you that I was going to do something and then not do it?" questioned Kit.

"No," the chief shook his head. "You always keep your word."

"Then you know that I will keep my word this time, too," said Kit. "Remember this—if the soldiers come to your camp I will be with them."

"I must have more time," protested Yellow Hand.

"I have given you five days and that is all the time I will give you," said Kit. He began to move toward his horse.

He turned to Billy. "Are you ready?" he asked.

"Yes, sir," Billy nodded. But to himself he said, "He has forgotten about Prince."

"This is a fine camp, Billy," said Kit as they mounted their horses. "Yellow Hand takes great pride in being a good chief to his people and he is also a wise chief. Do you like his camp?"

"Yes, I like it very much," was Billy's answer.

Kit smiled. "Yellow Hand," he said, "my friend,

Billy Cody, says he likes your camp very much."

Yellow Hand stepped forward. "I have many fine braves," he said.

"Which brave do you think is the finest warrior, Billy?" asked Kit.

"They are all fine braves," answered Billy. "But Yellow Hand, their chief, is the finest warrior of them all."

"White boy is young," smiled Yellow Hand, "but he speaks wise words."

Kit leaned forward in his saddle. "Yellow Hand," he said, "when you rode into the square I noticed the horse you were riding. Be sure that you return him with the others."

"Swift Eagle is my horse," said Yellow Hand.

"If he were an Indian pony I would believe you, but that horse belongs to a friend of mine," snapped Kit, "and he is to be returned. Do you understand? Two hundred and one horses are to be brought back to Fort Laramie."

Kit motioned to Billy. They touched their horses lightly and galloped from the square.

Billy Saves a Wagon Train

KIT and Billy headed back to Fort Laramie. When it was almost dark they turned off the trail, hobbled their horses and made camp for the night. They did not build a fire. They ate cold meat and dry bread for their supper.

"Mr. Carson," asked Billy as they stretched out on the ground to go to sleep, "do you think Yellow Hand will return the horses?"

"I feel quite sure that he will," answered Kit.

"And Prince, too?"

"Prince will be returned if the other horses are brought back." A few minutes later Kit added, "I did not know that Yellow Hand was riding Prince until you gave me our sign. That was good work, Billy."

But Billy did not hear Kit's praise. He was already sound asleep. Kit smiled, looked up at the bright stars and soon he, too, was asleep.

48

The next five days were long, anxious days for Billy. He was encouraged by Kit's demand that the horses be returned. Yet he remembered that Kit had never said positively that Yellow Hand would bring them back. Sometimes Billy was certain that the Indians would return all the horses. Then again he was filled with fear that all the horses except Prince would be returned.

Each day when Billy finished his work he hurried to the fort to look for Kit Carson. If he did not find Kit at the fort, Billy hurried to the Indian camps. And there in one of the camps Kit was most often to be found. He and a silent group of braves carried on long talks without speaking a word. They used the sign language. Their hands made the signs clearly and swiftly. Billy was spellbound as he stood quietly by and watched Kit and the Indians.

Then when the long talks were over, Kit and Billy would walk back to the fort. Each day Billy asked the same old question. "Will Yellow Hand return Prince and the other horses?"

Kit's answer was always the same. "We will

have to wait, Billy. I think Yellow Hand will bring Prince and the horses to the fort. But I am not sure. I don't trust Yellow Hand."

Five long, anxious days for Billy!

Then at last the fifth day passed. Just at sunset, a band of yelling Indians driving a herd of horses neared the fort. Men and soldiers rushed to a big corral. Billy was in the lead.

"The horses!" he shouted. "The horses!"

The gate was opened and the herd was driven into the corral. Billy climbed up on the gate. His keen eyes flashed from horse to horse as he searched for Prince. But Billy could not find Prince among the frightened horses racing about the corral.

"Prince," he called. His heart pounded so that he could scarcely breathe.

"Prince," he called again.

This time a whinny answered his call. And a beautiful brown horse with a star on his forehead pushed through the herd toward his master. Billy leaned over the gate. His arms went around Prince's neck.

"Prince, Prince," he whispered again and again.

He patted the horse and ran his fingers through the silky mane. "Yellow Hand has taken good care of you, but I don't forgive him for taking you away from me."

Suddenly Billy turned and looked for Kit. The slim, blue-eyed scout was standing nearby.

"Mr. Carson," shouted Billy, "here he is. This is Prince."

"You hardly need to tell me that," smiled Kit as he came forward. "Even the papooses in Yellow Hand's camp would know that Prince is your horse."

Later that evening Kit said, "Billy, my work here is finished. I am leaving in the morning with Simpson and his fifteen wagons for Fort Bridger. Don't forget that to be a good plains scout you must learn everything you can about the Indians and the plains."

"I won't forget, Mr. Carson."

"The Sioux chief, Rain-in-the-Face, and his Indians camped near the fort today. They intend to stay here several months. The chief has a son about your age. His name is Red Hawk. I think you would like this young brave. Spend as much time as you can with him and his friends."

"I will," nodded Billy. "Mr. Carson, I hope we'll meet again soon. But no matter if it is a long time before I see you again, I will never forget you."

"We will meet again, Billy. The trails are long and the forts are far apart, but here in the West old friends always meet again—somewhere."

Kit held out his hand and said, "Good-by, Billy."

"Good-by, Mr. Carson," said Billy as he shook hands with the famous scout. "Thanks for getting Prince back for me."

"I am glad that I could do it. Good luck, Billy."

Billy made friends with Red Hawk and the other young braves of the Sioux camp. They galloped their horses across the plains in wild, exciting races and Prince was the winner of most of the races. They followed trails and hunted together. The Sioux braves taught Billy many signs used in the sign language of the plains. They also taught him to speak the language of their tribe.

Red Hawk was Billy's best friend. The young brave was an expert hunter and trapper. He and

Billy often went hunting together.

One day when Billy and Red Hawk were out hunting, they met a small wagon train. The boys joined the wagon boss and rode with him ahead of the train.

"What is your name and what outfit are you with, son?" asked the wagon boss.

"I am Billy Cody and I am with Lew Simpson's wagon train. My friend is Red Hawk, the son of Chief Rain-in-the-Face."

"Rain-in-the-Face!" exclaimed the wagon boss. "The old Sioux chief at Fort Laramie? I am surprised he would let his son be a friend of a white boy. Better watch out for the chief. You don't want to lose your scalp, do you?"

"The Sioux are good Indians," defended Billy.

"You won't think so when they attack your wagon train," grinned the wagon boss. "Is Lew Simpson at Fort Laramie?"

"No," answered Billy. "He has gone on to Fort Bridger."

"Good. Then I'll see him there."

"Are you headed for Fort Bridger?" asked Billy.

"No, we are headed for Oregon. And if I ever get this train through, it will be the last train I'll take out for some time."

"Why?" asked Billy.

"I need a long rest," laughed the wagon boss. "I am taking ten families of settlers to Oregon and not one of them has ever been on the plains before. They hired me as their wagon boss. But I am the cook, doctor, fire builder, scout, nurse maid, guard, wagon mender, and"—he was silent for a moment—"minister," he added. "Yesterday a little girl died. I buried her and marked her grave."

Billy turned in his saddle and looked back at the covered wagons slowly coming on over the trail. In the first wagon, a young mother holding a baby in her arms smiled at him. She was pretty in her gay sunbonnet and flowered calico dress. On the driver's seat beside her was a boy about seven years old. He was driving the ox team. A man, gun in hand, walked along beside the wagon.

"Billy," said the wagon boss, "I have made many trips across the plains, but this trip is the most difficult one I have ever made."

"Have you had any Indian trouble?" asked Billy.

"No," the man shook his head, "I have had settler trouble."

"I don't understand," said Billy.

"Well, you see Billy, these people are very anxious to get to Oregon. They overlook the fact that it takes weeks, often months, to cross the plains. They are brave and they want to do their share of the work. But they had to learn that the success of a trip depends upon the help of everyone with the train.

"At first, I had to watch them carefully. They tried to drive their teams too hard and did not want to stop to rest during the day. At night they would forget to guard their animals. If I left them to find a good place to ford a river or a stream, they would sometimes try to cross before I returned and would get into trouble.

"At first, they saw no reason to form a circle with their wagons when we made camp. But one day we passed a burned wagon train. Since then I have had less trouble about getting them to camp properly."

At noon, the wagon boss ordered a halt. The drivers swung their wagons into position. The women hurried to prepare the noonday meal while the men cared for the animals. Laughing children ran in and out among the wagons, playing tag.

The boy in the first wagon unyoked his oxen and crawled back upon the driver's seat. His mother patted his head.

"I wonder what is the matter with Tommy," said the wagon boss. "I hope he isn't sick. Billy," he asked, "won't you and Red Hawk stay and eat with us?"

"No, thank you," answered Billy. "We started out to find a buffalo herd. We must be on our way."

"Well, I will see you at the fort," the wagon boss called over his shoulder as he rode to the circle. Billy and Red Hawk rode off across the plain.

Shortly after leaving the wagon train, the boys came to the top of a small rolling hill. Instantly both boys reined in their horses.

"Look over there!" exclaimed Billy, pointing at a cloud of dust rising from the plain. "Buffalo! And they are headed this way!"

Red Hawk cupped an ear with his right hand "Listen!" he said.

The two boys sat motionless. The distant rumble of thousands of hoofs came to their ears.

"A stampede!" shouted Billy. "A big herd on a wild stampede!"

The sound of pounding hoofs became a deep rumble. It grew louder and louder. Straight across the plains roared the herd of maddened buffalo.

"The wagon train!" cried Billy. "It's in the path of the stampede. The settlers will all be killed."

In a flash, the boys whirled their horses and raced back to the train.

"Stampede!" shouted Billy. "Headed this way! Stampede! Coming this way!"

"Quick!" shouted Red Hawk, waving his arms in warning.

The wagon boss shouted sharp orders. Everyone in the train dashed quickly to his post. Already the dark forms of the buffalo were charging over the hill.

The women and children hurriedly climbed into the wagons. The wagon boss posted the men as a

guard in front of the wagon train. Billy and Red Hawk quickly tied their horses inside the circle, and hurried to join the men. They all stood with rifles ready to fire at the advancing herd.

As the leaders came racing forward, the wagon boss ordered, "Pick the leaders in the center. Fire!"

Four huge buffalo leaders fell dead. Again and again the men fired. Again and again the leaders fell in front of the advancing herd. Their huge bodies made a mound and the herd was split. To

avoid the dead buffalo, part of the herd swerved to
the right and part to the left. Thousands plunged
by each side of the wagon train. They came so close
that some of them brushed against the sides of the
wagons. The force of the glancing blows shook the
wagons as though they were toy wagons.

Dust and a heavy smell filled the air. Everyone
was coughing and choking. The earth shook with
the heavy thunder of pounding hoofs.

Hour after hour the maddened herd swept on.
Hour after hour Billy and Red Hawk stood guard

with the men. Often a shot was needed to keep the wild herd separated.

Finally the last of the herd thundered by. The wagon train was once again alone on the prairie.

Everything was covered with a thick, heavy dust. On each side of the wagon train the grass and sagebrush had been trampled flat on the ground.

Now that the danger was over, everyone began talking and laughing at once.

"Billy, we owe our lives to your prompt warning," said the wagon boss.

"Don't forget my friend, Red Hawk," smiled Billy. "He helped as much as I did."

"Yes, I know," said the wagon boss. He scratched his head and grinned. "The next time the Sioux Indians attack me I'll try to remember that at least one Sioux brave helped save my life instead of trying to get my scalp."

Through the opening of one wagon the young mother with the gay sunbonnet looked out. Her eyes were wide with terror.

Billy hurried to her. "Are you all right, lady?" he asked.

"I think I am now," she smiled down at him, "but I was scared to death."

"Mary," called a man running toward the wagon, "are you and the children all right?"

"Yes, John," she answered, "but Tommy is too ill to drive any more today."

"I will drive for you," spoke up Billy.

"That would be a great help," said the man. "The wagon boss has ordered me to go on ahead with him. I must go now, Mary," he added. "Take care of Tommy."

"I will be back in a few minutes," said Billy. "I must get my horse."

Red Hawk, holding Prince, was waiting for Billy.

"I am going to drive one of the wagons," said Billy. "You ride on ahead to the fort and tell the men of my outfit where I am and that I'll be in later."

Red Hawk nodded. "I will tell them, but when are we going to hunt buffalo?"

Billy laughed. "I have seen all the buffalo I want to see for one day."

A Narrow Escape

THE SETTLERS had to spend a week at Fort Laramie. They repaired their wagons and rested their animals. Then they continued on their way westward to Oregon. Tommy, now well and strong, was back on the driver's seat of his wagon as the train moved slowly away over the plain.

Several weeks later Simpson returned to Fort Laramie. He sent for Billy as soon as he reached the fort.

"Billy," he said, "I met an old friend who is on his way to Oregon with a train of settlers. He told me how you and Red Hawk saved his train from a buffalo stampede. He and all the settlers had much to say about you. I have decided to give you a new job with my wagon train."

"Thank you, Mr. Simpson."

"It will be an important job but you can do it. I am taking two large wagon trains back to

Leavenworth. The trains will travel in separate sections, one day apart. I need someone to scout ahead, to locate camping places, and to carry messages from one train to the other. Do you want to try it?"

"Yes, I do, sir," answered Billy quickly.

"It will mean that you will be on the trail alone much of the time. You may meet hostile Indians, and you will have to depend upon yourself to get away from them. You will watch for Indian signs, and keep the wagon drivers informed of anything suspicious that you see."

"That is almost like being a regular scout, isn't it?" asked Billy.

Simpson nodded.

"That's what I want to be!" exclaimed Billy. "I want to be a scout like Kit Carson."

Simpson laughed, but he said quietly, "I know you do, Billy, and that's why I am giving you this chance. You have a good rifle, but now you will need a bowie knife and a brace of revolvers. I will get them for you here at the trading post. They shall be yours if you make good on this trip. And, in the spring, I will make you one of my regular scouts."

"Oh, thank you, Mr. Simpson. I have always wanted a pair of matched revolvers," smiled Billy. He looked up quickly and asked, "Will I have to wait until spring to be one of your regular scouts?"

"This will be my last trip this year," explained Simpson. "I must get as many wagons as I can back to Leavenworth. We never have enough wagons when the spring rush starts westward."

A few days later, the first section of the wagon train left Fort Laramie. The long line of white-topped wagons stretched out over the trail. Two hundred men traveled with the section. Some of the men were mounted on mules or horses, but most of them walked beside the wagons.

The next morning, the second section was on its way. Billy, mounted on Prince, rode with Simpson in front of the lead wagon.

"Billy," said Simpson, "your horse is too good a horse to ride every day. You had better ride a mule most of the trip. I have some extra mules with each section for you to use."

"I won't ride Prince every day," said Billy. "But I wanted to ride my own horse the first day on my new job."

"When we halt at noon, you are to ride on to the first section, Billy," said Simpson. "Tell the wagon boss that we are following them."

"Shall I report back to you?" asked Billy.

"No, stay with the first section tonight," answered Simpson. "In the morning ride on ahead for about fifteen miles. While looking for signs of Indians, keep your eyes open for a camping place where there is enough grass to feed our animals." He shook his head as he continued, "There has been a lot of travel on the trail this year and I'm afraid there isn't very much grass left. Do this each morning that you are with the first section and report back to me each day."

"Yes, sir," said Billy.

Day after day the sections moved on over the trail. Billy rode back and forth with his reports to Simpson. Sometimes Simpson rode ahead with him, but most of the time Billy made his trips alone.

One day, Billy returned to the first section from his usual scouting trip. Finding Simpson with this section, Billy reported, "Mr. Simpson, there isn't enough grass on the trail to feed our animals. I even left the trail and rode southward a few miles but found nothing."

"That is what I feared," said Simpson. "Well, we'll have to leave this trail and follow the route along the North Platte River. I had hoped to avoid the northern route because of the chance of running into Indian trouble. But our animals must have food. From now on, Billy, watch even more carefully for Indian signs. And never ride away from camp without your rifle, revolvers, and plenty of ammunition."

Billy was careful and cautious. Each day, as he scouted ahead or rode between the two sections, he watched for signs. He carried his rifle ready for action. He wore the brace of revolvers buckled snugly around his slim waist. On the trail he was always alert for danger. In camp he was always ready to do more than his share of the work.

Every man with both sections was Billy's friend.

All the men were experienced plainsmen, and many of them were rough in manners and speech. But they were fond of Billy and each day as they sighted the young rider galloping toward their section they greeted him with friendly shouts. They felt a little easier and a little less anxious for the boy when he was near, though they did not say so.

One day about noon, Billy, Simpson, and a man by the name of George Woods left together to join the first section. All three were mounted on mules. When they had ridden about twelve miles Billy suddenly pulled his mule to a stop.

"What is the matter, Billy?" asked Simpson.

"I thought I saw something moving," answered Billy. He pointed to the top of a hill in the distance.

"I don't see anything," said Woods, "except the sagebrush."

"There!" exclaimed Billy, "a horse and a rider. He's gone again. He rides his horse in a circle and then disappears. You know that's the sign many Indians use to let their braves know when to make an attack."

"You're right, Billy," snapped Simpson. "I see

him now. We are in for some real trouble."

At this moment, a bloodcurdling war whoop split the air. Over the hill raced a band of warriors. Their war bonnets of eagle feathers streamed out in the wind.

"Lead the mules together so that they will make a triangle," shouted Simpson as he jumped from his saddle. "Our only chance is to shoot the mules and use their bodies for a fort."

Simpson's and Wood's revolvers barked. "Quick, Billy," ordered Simpson, "there is no time to lose."

Billy obeyed. The bodies of the three mules now lay on the ground in the form of a triangle. The men fell to the ground in the center.

The Indians were almost within range. Arrows began to whiz through the air.

"Use your rifles," ordered Simpson. "Fire when they begin to close in on us. Now," he added, "let's get the three leaders."

The rifles blazed. Three Indians fell to the ground and their ponies raced madly away.

"Fire!" commanded Simpson, and again three

riderless ponies ran loose over the plain.

Yelling and shouting, the Indians fell back.

"They'll be back in a minute," said Simpson. "Keep using your rifles to hold them as far off as possible, but have your revolvers ready. Billy, are you all right?"

"Yes, sir," answered Billy without taking his eyes off the Indians. "I'm glad I wasn't riding Prince today."

In spite of their danger Simpson laughed, "Surrounded by Indians who are trying to kill us, and all you can think of is that you are glad that you weren't riding Prince."

"Get ready, here they come," called Woods.

Time and again the Indians swooped straight down upon them. Each time, three rifles cracked and three Indians fell to the ground and lay still. So far, Billy and the men had not missed a shot. But the Indians kept up the attack. Leaning low over the sides of their ponies and using them as shields, the Indians would dash forward, let fly their arrows, and race away again.

"They can't get us by charging," said Woods.

"No," Simpson gritted his teeth, "but now they will begin to circle us."

The Indians spread out to form a huge circle. At a signal from their chief, the yelling braves began to close in. Billy's rifle was firing steadily on his side of the "fort."

"That's right, Billy," shouted Simpson, "get one with every shot." As he spoke, he aimed his rifle carefully and fired.

"If we live to get back to Leavenworth," continued Simpson, "you can have a job as regular scout with me anytime you want it, Billy."

Billy grinned in answer as he squeezed the trigger of his rifle.

The Indians again retreated, but in a few minutes they attacked with renewed fury.

An arrow struck Woods in the arm.

"Which one of you redskins did that?" he asked as he dropped his rifle. "No, Billy," he said, "keep your eyes on the Indians. I'll take care of myself."

Slowly he withdrew the arrow so as not to break the shaft and leave the arrowhead buried in his arm. He tore a strip of cloth from his faded, blue shirt and wrapped it tightly around the bleeding wound.

"Poisoned arrow?" asked Simpson without turning around.

"No, and lucky for me," answered Woods picking up his rifle. He took careful aim and fired.

"Didn't hurt my aim," he chuckled.

Darkness began to fall and the Indians withdrew to a safe distance from the range of the white men's rifles.

"That means the attacks are over for today," said Simpson. "Look at our poor mules. They are stuck so full of arrows they look like pincushions."

"I believe these are Cheyenne arrows," said Billy. "See the marks on them?"

"That may mean that Yellow Hand—"

"Yellow Hand!" exclaimed Billy. "Kit Carson made him return some stolen horses to Fort Laramie this summer."

"Yes, and if I know Yellow Hand, he is out to get revenge," said Woods. "He is a tricky and a dangerous enemy."

The Indians made camp. Their campfires blazed

and brightened the sky. Their guards surrounded the white men at a safe distance while the other braves danced around the campfire.

"I don't think they will attack during the night," said Simpson, "but we had better stay awake. If we can hold out for a few hours in the morning the second wagon train will come along and save us."

"Let me try to slip through the guards and get word back to our outfit."

"No, Billy," said Simpson, "our best chance is to try to hold out until the train reaches us."

"But let me try," pleaded Billy.

"No," Simpson's voice was firm. "I need you and your rifle here, Billy. I don't know what we would do without you. You are certainly a crack shot."

It was late when the Indian camp became quiet. The Indian guards, however, remained on duty.

In the morning, when the first rays of light appeared in the east, the Indians were astir. Just at sunrise, they renewed their attack. Yelling and shouting their war whoops, they circled and then began to close in on the mule fort. Three blazing rifles stopped them and sent them retreating out of range.

"They will try to make us use up all our ammunition," said Simpson. "Then they will ride in for the kill."

"Why doesn't our wagon train come along?" asked Woods. "Do you suppose they were attacked by Indians after we left them yesterday?"

"I don't know," answered Simpson, "but let's hope they started early this morning."

Slowly the morning hours dragged on. Several times the Indians made quick, sharp attacks. Each time they were forced back by blazing rifles.

Suddenly Billy jumped to his feet and shouted. Simpson grabbed him and pulled him roughly to the ground.

"What in the world is the matter with you?" he asked. "Are you trying to get killed?"

"No," said Billy, "but I heard the crack of a bull whip. It's our train! They are coming!"

Simpson and Woods looked at each other and the two men shook their heads.

"Look!" shouted Billy. "The Indians hear it,

too. They have all stopped and are listening."

"You're right, Billy!" exclaimed Simpson, "but the Indians will make one last attack. Get ready!"

Once again the Indians charged down upon them. Yells and war whoops rang out. Tomahawks were hurled straight at the mule fort as the Indians dashed by.

Now the cracks of the bull whips could be plainly heard. The Indians made one final swoop past the mule fort and raced away.

Down the hill came the mounted men of the wagon train. As they galloped toward the mule fort their rifles blazed into the retreating Indians.

Billy ran to meet the men. Simpson and Woods leaned back against the body of a dead mule and called, "Good morning, boys. Thanks for coming up on time."

A halt was called and the men crowded around the mule fort. Simpson told them how they had been attacked and as he finished he turned to Billy and said, "The revolvers are yours, Billy, and anything else you want."

"What will it be, Billy?" laughed the men.

For a minute Billy hesitated. Then he said, "Billy is a boy's name. I want to be called Bill."

Simpson slapped him on the shoulder. "Bill," he said, "if I ever hear anyone call you anything but Bill from now on he will have to answer to me. Boys," he cried, "a cheer for Bill Cody!"

"Hurrah!" shouted the men. "Hurrah for Bill Cody!"

Trapping on Prairie Creek

DAY AFTER DAY, the wagon train pushed on over the rolling plains. Day after day, Bill Cody rode the trail keeping watch for signs of trouble. At last the train neared Leavenworth.

"Bill," asked Simpson, "don't we pass your cabin on this trail?"

"Yes, sir," answered Bill. "We are only a few miles from my home."

"There is no need for you to go on with the train," said Simpson. "Ride on home. Someone is there who will be glad to see you."

"Thank you, Mr. Simpson."

Bill touched Prince lightly. The horse broke into a long, easy gallop. When they reached the turn in the trail the Cody cabin came into view. A smile flashed across Bill's sun-tanned face and he leaned forward in the saddle. He urged Prince to greater speed. Prince laid back his ears and raced down

77

the old familiar path toward the cabin.

"Mother," called Bill. "Mother!"

In an instant Mrs. Cody appeared in the doorway of the cabin. Four little girls in long blue
dresses crowded around her.

"Billy!" the girls cried as they ran to meet their
brother.

"Billy, my son!" called Mrs. Cody. Her gentle
happy smile met the laughter in her son's brown
eyes. She held out her arms. Billy reined in Prince
and sprang from the saddle.

It was late that night before the Cody family
went to sleep. Bill told his mother and sisters about
the trip—how Kit Carson made the Indians return
Prince, how he and Red Hawk warned the settlers'
train, and many other stories about the men with
the wagon trains and about Lew Simpson.

"Mr. Simpson gave me these revolvers because
I—" He stopped and said to himself, "If I tell
Mother about the Indian fight she would worry
even more about me. I know my sisters would en-
joy the excitement but I don't want to frighten
Mother."

"Why did Mr. Simpson give you the revolvers?" asked Mrs. Cody.

"Because I am to be a scout," answered Bill.

Mrs. Cody was silent. Bill and his sisters laughed and talked. When the girls had gone to bed his mother asked, "Billy, do you really want to be a scout?"

"Yes, Mother, I do."

"Then promise me one thing, Billy: be a good scout." She smiled, but there were tears in her eyes.

Bill loved his mother and sisters. He was glad to be home again. But the life on the plains had filled his restless young heart.

One day when he returned from Leavenworth he said to his mother, "I saw Dave Harrington today. You remember him, don't you?"

Mrs. Cody nodded. "Yes, Dave is a fine young man. He is a trapper, isn't he?"

"Yes, and this winter he wants to trap at Prairie Creek about two hundred miles west of here. He needs someone to go with him who knows the trails."

"And he asked you to go with him," smiled Mrs. Cody. "And you told him you would go."

"How did you know?"

Mrs. Cody laughed, "Oh, Billy," she said, "I can see the light in your eyes whenever you speak of the plains. When do you and Dave plan to leave?"

"As soon as we can buy the supplies we need," answered Bill. "We will be gone all winter. You see, Mother, I won't have another job with a wagon train until spring. But if I go with Dave I will earn some money this winter, and that will make it easier for you."

"Billy, you gave me all the money you earned on your trip with Mr. Simpson and it is enough for a long time."

"I know, Mother, but I want to take good care of you and my sisters."

"I am very proud of you, my son."

The next few days were busy days for Bill and Dave. They bought a wagon and a yoke of oxen. They bought flour, bacon, beans, and other food supplies. They loaded the wagon with their supplies, with traps of many kinds, and with barrels of salt to cure the hides of the animals they would trap.

Dave stayed with the Cody family the night before the boys left on their trip. Mrs. Cody and the girls packed several boxes of cookies and bread for the boys.

Bill and Dave were sitting in front of the fireplace oiling their rifles.

"Do you want to take some books with you, Billy?" asked Mrs. Cody.

"Oh, yes," answered Bill. "We will have a lot of time to read during the long winter nights."

"Pick out the books you want to take," said Mrs. Cody, "and I will put them in this box."

"I'll pack them, Mother," said Bill jumping to his feet. "You sit here and rest awhile."

In the morning Bill and Dave were on their way to Prairie Creek. The boys had a good time as they traveled slowly westward. They met a number of wagon trains returning to Leavenworth for the winter months. Stagecoaches, with their horses galloping at full speed, rattled by them on the trail. The clatter of the horses' hoofs and the cheery greetings of the drivers as they dashed by always thrilled Bill. Now and then, they met a wagon train of weary settlers who had become discouraged and were returning to their homes in the East.

One night the boys stopped at a settler's cabin near the trail. The man, his wife, and children asked the boys to eat supper and spend the night with them. Bill and Dave readily accepted the invitation.

"Where are you going?" asked the man.

"We are headed for Prairie Creek," answered Bill. "We are going to trap there this winter."

"You will have a good season," said the man. "The creeks and streams are full of beaver and otter. Better watch out for Indians though."

The boys laughed. "We will," they promised.

"How far is it to Prairie Creek?" asked Bill.

"Well," the man scratched his head, "you are a hundred miles from Leavenworth. You are still about a hundred and twenty-five miles from Prairie Creek."

"Will we pass any more cabins on the way?" asked Bill.

"No, sir," answered the settler. "Ours is the last cabin on the trail. When you come back, plan to stay with us for a few days. We get lonely sometimes. But," he added quickly, "we wouldn't trade our cabin for the finest house in Leavenworth."

The next morning, Bill and Dave said good-by to their friends and set out for Prairie Creek.

When the boys reached the place they had chosen for their trapping ground, they built a dugout to use for their living quarters, and a corral for their oxen.

The dugout was built in the side of a hill. It had two small windows and a door. Its roof was made of brush and long grass with a covering of earth. There was a small fireplace in one wall of the dugout to be used for both heating and cooking.

When the boys had completed the corral for the oxen, they set their traps along the creek banks. Early each morning they inspected their traps. They reset those that had been sprung and carried back to the dugout the beaver and otter caught during the night. Then they spent the rest of the day skinning the animals and salting the hides.

One night after supper, Bill and Dave were lying in front of the fireplace reading.

Suddenly Dave jumped to his feet. "What was that?" he asked. He grabbed his rifle and ran outside.

Bill, gun in hand, followed quickly. As he ran around the corner of the dugout Dave's rifle flashed. Down by the corral a growling bear turned and standing on his hind legs charged toward Dave. Instantly Bill raised his gun and fired. The bear fell dead at Dave's feet.

"Good shot, Bill," said Dave. "Thanks for saving my hide."

"You can do the same for me sometime," laughed Bill. "Come, let's see what happened to our oxen."

The boys hurried to the corral. One ox was badly torn by the bear's sharp claws and had to be shot.

"We will have to get another ox before we can get our furs home," said Dave as they walked back to the dugout. "But we don't have to worry about that now."

"I am sure the old settler with whom we spent the night will sell us an ox," said Bill. "I will go to him later and ask him to help us."

In the morning as usual, the boys were up early. They ate breakfast and left the dugout to inspect their traps. On the way, they sighted a large herd of elk.

"Let's get one," said Bill.

They crept along the creek bank to get close enough to the herd to get a good shot. Bill tripped over a stone and fell to the ground. He started to rise, but fell back groaning with pain.

"Bill, what's the matter?" called Dave.

"I think I have broken my leg."

Dave examined Bill's leg. "You are right," he said shaking his head, "your leg is broken."

Dave carried Bill back to the dugout. He made a splint out of a wagon bow and set Bill's leg. Dave was careful, but Bill winced with pain whenever Dave moved his leg.

"This accident changes our plans," said Dave. "I must get you out of here as soon as I can."

"Why?" asked Bill. "I know I can't help with the traps, but I can work here in the dugout. Can't we stay a few more weeks and try out my plan?"

"No," was Dave's firm reply. "If Indians attack they could kill both of us. As long as we could both leave the dugout and travel on foot we could take care of ourselves. Now, it's different."

"I guess you are right," replied Bill, "and I won't insist on our staying. I don't want to endanger either your life or mine."

"Good. Now this is what I plan to do," said Dave. "I will go back to the old settler to see if I can buy a yoke of oxen from him. We must return to Leavenworth before we get snowed in. I'll let our ox out of the corral before I leave. You won't be able to feed and water him so he will have to shift for himself. I don't like to leave you here alone."

"Don't bother about me," broke in Bill, "I'll be all right."

"I am not so sure. I am afraid that I may be gone about three weeks."

"I know," nodded Bill. "But I can take care of myself. Before you leave you can put everything I will need near my bunk so I can reach it."

"Good for you, Bill."

Dave went to work to make the dugout comfortable for Bill while he was gone. He pulled Bill's bunk over to the fireplace and put the food supplies within easy reach. He chopped wood and piled it beside the fireplace. Extra blankets and the box of books were also placed within reach of the bunk.

"Well," he said when he had finished, "I guess I have taken care of everything. And the sooner I get started the sooner I will return."

Bill, lying on the bunk, looked up at Dave. "I am sorry that you have to take this long, hard trip alone," he said. "I'll be thinking about you."

Dave grinned. "Wait until next winter. I'll send you out to bring in the skins and set all the traps while I lie in bed. Good-by, Bill."

"Good-by and good luck, Dave."

The door closed and Bill was alone. For a while he lay staring up at the roof of the dugout. The room was very quiet and he soon fell asleep. It was dark when he awakened. Far away the howl of a wolf echoed and died away.

Alone in a Blizzard

BILL DID not eat any supper. The deep dull ache of his broken leg was almost unbearable. Several times he reached for a piece of wood to put on the dying fire. Each time the effort made him groan with pain.

"It's no use," he said to himself, "I can't do it."

He tried to go to sleep again. He was sure that he could not. But in the morning the first light of day crept in through the windows of the dugout and fell on the golden curly hair of a sleeping boy.

When Bill awakened, he was feeling better. The pain in his leg was still severe, but he was hungry.

"That's a good sign," he said, laughing a little as he eased himself to the edge of the bunk. "I'll start a fire and cook breakfast."

He had to be careful so as not to move his leg. It took him a long time to build the fire and to cook his breakfast.

"Dave certainly put everything I need within reach," he said to himself. "I hope he doesn't have a hard trip. He said that it would take him about twenty days to make the trip, but I wonder how many days it will really take him to do it."

Slowly the days and nights dragged on. Bill kept a record of the days by cutting a notch in a stick for each day. He spent most of his time reading the books which he had brought with him on the trip.

One morning, Bill was awakened by the touch of a hand on his shoulder.

"Dave!" he exclaimed, "are you—?" The words died on his lips.

Bending over him was an Indian brave. Four other warriors stood at the foot of his bunk. All were in full war paint. Quivers filled with arrows hung at their left sides and each carried a long bow and a tomahawk. The feathers of their war bonnets almost touched the roof of the dugout.

Bill held his breath. Then slowly he pulled himself to a sitting position.

"Why are you here?" he demanded.

The warriors stood silent and motionless.

The door opened and other warriors entered the little room. They crowded around the bunk. The braves talked together in low voices.

Bill leaned forward. "They are Sioux," he said to himself.

"We wait for chief," said a brave, "then we kill white boy."

"I will not let them know that I understand their language," Bill said to himself. "I, too, will wait for chief."

Suddenly from outside came the sounds of galloping horses and a Sioux war whoop. The braves rushed to the door and shouted to the Indians on horseback. The horses were reined in by the door of the dugout. Then there was silence.

A tall, dignified old chief entered the dugout and gave an order. Instantly the braves by Bill's bunk moved aside. Their chief strode toward Bill.

"Rain-in-the-Face," smiled Bill to himself. "I am in luck." But his smile disappeared when he looked into the cold eyes of the old chief.

"We take food and guns from white boy," said

the chief without taking his eyes off Bill. "We go."

"No," spoke up a brave. "We kill white boy. See long yellow hair. Make nice scalp."

The chief shrugged his shoulders.

"Chief Rain-in-the-Face, don't you remember me?" asked Bill.

"You speak Sioux?" exclaimed the chief.

"Yes," nodded Bill. "Don't you remember me?"

"No."

"Your son is my friend. I am Bill Cody."

"I don't know you," said the chief coldly.

"I met your son at Fort Laramie," explained Bill. "We are good friends. I have many friends among your young braves."

"I remember now," said the chief. "You here alone?"

"Yes," answered Bill. "I broke my leg." He pointed to the bandaged leg and continued, "You would not kill a boy who is unable to defend himself. You are a Sioux chief."

"My braves say we kill white boy."

"They will obey your orders. You are their chief."

Chief Rain-in-the-Face turned to his braves and said, "We not kill white boy."

The braves protested.

"Silence!" thundered the chief. "We not kill white boy," he repeated. "We take food and guns."

"If you take my food I will starve to death," broke in Bill. "You may as well kill me as to do that."

"I spare your life," said the chief. "I leave some meat. That is all. Give me your guns."

Bill made no move to obey the chief's order.

"Give me your guns!"

Bill turned back the blankets on his bunk and slowly uncovered the brace of revolvers and his rifle. He handed them to the chief.

"Ugh," grunted the chief. He gave Bill's rifle to a brave. "Fine guns," he nodded as he buckled Bill's brace of revolvers around his waist. Then without another word he turned, signaled to his braves, and left the dugout.

Silently Bill watched the Indians take his food, matches, ammunition, and some of his clothes. When they had taken everything they wanted they left the dugout, mounted their horses, and rode away.

"Now, what am I going to do?" Bill asked himself. "They didn't leave me enough meat to last a week. And I'll have to keep the fire going day and night for I have no matches. How many days has Dave been gone?" he asked reaching for the stick. "Eleven days. This is the twelfth," he added, and cut another notch in the stick. "That means eight more days before I can expect Dave back."

Two days later a heavy snowstorm swept over Prairie Creek. It snowed all day. Great drifts covered the windows and blocked the doorway. The wind blew the snow through the cracks of the dugout. The snow made the firewood wet and Bill had a difficult time trying to keep the fire going.

"This is bad," he said to himself. "I don't know how long this storm will last. It will delay Dave's return. He may not be able to get back at all. I thought the first days and nights would never come to an end but now—"

The storm stopped almost as quickly as it had begun. The howl of the wind died down. Once more the howls of the hungry wolves filled the night air.

Thirteen days, fourteen, fifteen, and then at last the twentieth day came. Bill was awake early. All day he listened for a sound that would tell him that Dave had returned. Slowly the long hours passed. Night came on and the only sounds were the howls of the wolves.

Bill was desperate. He was sick from hunger and worn out from loss of sleep.

"I could stand this," he said clenching his teeth, "if I only knew that Dave was all right. But I am afraid that something terrible has happened to him. He might be dead—frozen to death in this storm."

Twenty-five days, twenty-six, twenty-seven, twenty-eight days passed. And each day was a day of torture. The meat was gone and only a little wood was left for his fire.

"Twenty-nine days," said Bill as he cut another notch in the stick. Suddenly, he stiffened. The stick fell from his hands. "I thought I heard some-one," he said aloud.

"Hello, Bill," called a voice from outside.

"Dave!" shouted Bill. "Dave, are you really there?"

"Sure," Dave's laughing voice answered. "Are you all right, Bill?"

"I am fine," called Bill. He leaned back in his bunk and drew a deep breath. "I am fine—now."

"As soon as I clear the snow away from the door I'll be in," called Dave. "Get the fire going. I'm almost frozen."

Bill threw on the last of the wood. He had a big fire blazing by the time Dave flung open the door and rushed into the dugout.

"I am glad to see you," laughed Bill. "I was almost sure that you would never make it."

"So was I," grinned Dave holding his hands out to the warmth of the fire. "But how did you get along by yourself, Bill?"

"I'll tell you later. First, I want to hear about your trip."

Dave pulled a box over by the fireplace and sat down. "Well," he began, "I had a tough trip. I was caught in the blizzard and delayed three days. The trails were covered with snow. The drifts made it almost impossible to travel. Some days I walked less than five miles because of the deep snow.

"But here I am," he laughed, "and we'll start for home as soon as we can. The old settler was very kind to me. He sold me a yoke of oxen. And he wants us to spend a few days at his cabin on our way back home."

The boys laughed and talked for hours. Bill told

about his unexpected visit from Rain-in-the-Face and how the old chief had spared his life but had taken his guns. He told how the braves had taken most of his food and all of his matches. He told how he had to stay awake day and night to keep his fire burning.

"I was all right until the day of the blizzard," said Bill. "But I knew that you were out in it and from then on I have been worrying about you, Dave. I'll never forget what you have done for me. You risked your life to save mine."

"Forget it, Bill."

"But you did, Dave. You made a round trip on foot of two hundred and fifty miles to get help for me. Few men could have made the trip through that blizzard; and I'll never forget it."

Dave laughed. "It's a good thing that I brought some food back with me. The settler's wife insisted that I bring it to you. I didn't want to take it, but at that time I didn't know that you were going to give all our food to the Indians."

A few days later they started on the long trip back to Bill's home. Their furs were loaded in the wagon and Bill was lying on a bed inside the wagon. Dave drove the oxen.

"How many furs do we have?" asked Bill.

"Three hundred beaver skins," answered Dave, "and one hundred otter skins. We will sell them in Leavenworth and we will each make several hundred dollars."

"Good!" exclaimed Bill. "It wasn't such a bad trip after all, was it?"

"It was a fine trip," grinned Dave.

On the way they stopped at the old settler's cabin and stayed several days. They gave the settler twenty-five beaver skins to pay for the oxen. Then they said good-by to the settler and his family and headed for Leavenworth.

Ten days later they reached Bill's home. Bill told his mother and sisters how Dave had saved his life.

That night Mrs. Cody said to Dave, "I know your mother and father are dead and that you have no real home. I want you to make your home with us."

"Thank you," smiled Dave. "I shall be happy to

make my home here with the Cody family."

A few weeks later Dave became ill. Mrs. Cody sent Bill for the doctor. But, in spite of the medical attention and Mrs. Cody's constant nursing care, Dave grew steadily worse. Day and night for a week, Bill remained at Dave's bedside. He refused to believe that his friend would not get well. But early one morning Dave died.

"He was my friend, Mother," said Bill as he struggled to keep back the tears. "Dave was a real plainsman and I shall miss him."

The Pony Express

ONE NIGHT the Cody family were gathered around the fireplace of their little cabin. The girls were reading and Bill was lying on the floor staring into the flames of the fire. Now and then, Mrs. Cody looked up from her sewing and watched her son.

"Billy," she asked at last, "why are you so quiet tonight? Is it because you miss Dave?"

Bill nodded.

"We all miss him," said his mother gently. "Dave was a fine boy."

"I can't understand how he could live through that hard trip this winter, and then get sick here and die. I just can't believe it, Mother."

They were silent for a while. Then Bill said, "I am riding to Leavenworth tomorrow. I am going to sign up as a scout with Mr. Simpson's wagon train."

"But your leg, Billy," protested his mother, "you

still limp when you walk. I wish you wouldn't go to work this spring."

"The spring rush won't begin for a month and by that time I will be all right, Mother," said Bill.

The following morning, Bill mounted Prince and rode to Leavenworth. The little river town was alive with the excitement of getting ready for the spring rush. River steamers and barges lined the levees. Laborers hurried up and down the gang-planks unloading the supplies that were soon to be shipped overland by wagon trains. The levee was covered with great piles of freight. Some of the piles of freight were covered with great sheets of canvas, and some of the supplies were being hauled to the warehouses and stores. Yokes of oxen, pull-ing heavily loaded wagons, made their way slowly through the muddy streets. Mules, horses, and cattle were being herded into huge corrals.

The streets were filled with people. Fur trap-pers and blanketed Indians, with their packs of furs, crowded the trading posts. Soldiers from the nearby fort laughed and talked with the scouts of the wagon trains. Wagon bosses carefully looked over the newly repaired wagons and signed up the men who were to go with their trains. Boys, eager to join a wagon train, listened to the talk of the scouts and old plainsmen. Settlers, going west to make new homes, were buying teams, wagons, and supplies of food and clothing. Many newcomers had discarded their Eastern clothes for frontier outfits, but it was easy to tell them from the men of the plains.

Bill rode directly to the office of Russell, Majors & Waddell. He dismounted and tied Prince to a post.

"Hello, Bill," called Lew Simpson who was standing with a group of men nearby. "Did you come to sign up as scout with my train?"

Before Bill could answer, Frank McCarthy stepped forward and said, "The lad is going with my train."

"Bill is going with me," protested Simpson.

"I gave him his first job," broke in McCarthy. "He is going with me."

They were interrupted by Alec Majors. "I'll settle this argument," he laughed. "Bill Cody is not going with either of you. I have a special job for him. Come, Bill," he added, "I want to talk to you."

As Majors and Bill entered the building, Simpson said, "Majors wants Bill for that secret plan he has been working on this winter."

McCarthy nodded. "Yes, and it must be a job that calls for an expert rider and a crack shot, or Majors wouldn't have Bill Cody in mind for it."

Bill followed Majors into his office. When they were seated, Majors asked, "Bill, how would you like to be a Pony Express rider?"

"All right, I guess, Uncle Alec, but what is a Pony Express rider?"

"I'll explain it to you, Bill," began Majors. "Ever since the discovery of gold in California in 1849, people from the East and from everywhere have flocked to California. They believed that they would become rich in a few months and then would return to their old homes. Some of them did get rich quickly and some of them did return to their homes in the East. But most of the people did not get rich, and many of them decided to remain in the West and make new homes for their families.

"For several years, our firm has had a contract with the United States government to carry mail to and from California. Each year our stage-coaches have hauled millions of dollars worth of gold and other valuable express. Our men have done a splendid job. But now the people of California need and demand a faster mail service. We are going to give it to them.

"We have just made a new contract with the government to carry the mail between Sacramento, California, and St. Joseph, Missouri, where the railroad from the East has been completed. We have agreed that each trip will take only ten days."

"Ten days!" exclaimed Bill.

"Ten days!" repeated Majors.

"The stagecoaches can't make two thousand miles in ten days."

"You are right, Bill, but the Pony Express can do it."

Bill whistled. "I understand, Uncle Alec."

"Do you want to ride with the Pony Express?"

"Do I!" exclaimed Bill. "I certainly do."

"I knew you would," laughed Alec Majors.

"When do we start?"

"We expect to start the Overland Pony Express about the first of April."

"What about the stagecoaches?" asked Bill. "Will they still carry mail when the Pony Express begins?"

"Oh, yes," answered Majors. "You see, Bill, the Pony Express will carry only the most important mail. It will be too expensive for ordinary mail. The postage on even a single letter written on thin paper, if carried by the Pony Express, will cost five dollars."

"Why should it be so expensive?"

"A lot of people will ask that question," replied Majors. "The answer is that we must limit the amount of mail to be carried by each rider in order that his horse can keep up the necessary speed. To get the mail through in ten days will depend upon three things. It will depend upon the speed of the horses, the endurance of the riders, and the weight to be carried by the horses."

"That means we will have good horses."

"The very best!" exclaimed Majors, "and the fastest that money can buy. Some of them are full-blooded race horses from the East but most of them are sturdy, swift mustangs of the western plains. The speed of the horse is necessary to get the mail through on time. But it is also important because the life of the rider may often depend upon how fast he can get away from Indians or outlaws. I don't expect the riders of the Pony Express to shoot their way out of trouble. I expect them to outrun trouble and bring the mail through."

"We will do that, Uncle Alec."

"I am sure you will," agreed Majors. "We have hired the best horsemen in the West to become Pony Express riders. They are all young, light in weight, and fearless. You will be the youngest rider, but I believe that you can ride with the best of them."

"Thank you, Uncle Alec," smiled Bill. "This is a big undertaking, isn't it?"

"Yes," Majors answered slowly. "It is the biggest job I ever hope to do. And it will all be over in about two years."

"Why?" questioned Bill.

"When the telegraph lines are completed, there will be no further need for the Pony Express," answered Majors. "The line from the East has already been completed to St. Joseph and the line from the West is now being built. When the line is completed between the East and the West, the days of the Pony Express will be over. But in the meantime, the Pony Express will operate over a two-thousand-mile trail. The trail will cross the rolling plains, the deserts, and two high mountain ranges."

"Will the Pony Express have relay stations and home stations and be divided into sections like the stagecoach lines?"

"Yes, we have a hundred and ninety stations about fifteen miles apart all along the trail for the Pony Express riders. Each relay station will have a station agent who will take care of the horses. At the home stations the Pony Express riders will eat and sleep. Each section will be in charge of a section boss. He will be responsible for the stations and the riders of his section.

"You will be stationed at Julesburg on the trail

to Fort Laramie. Your section is called the Sweet-water section. A rider will bring the mail from the East to Julesburg and you will take it on west for fifty miles. There are three relay stations on your route where you will stop to get fresh horses. At the last station you will meet the rider bringing the mail from the West. You will exchange mail with him and then ride back to Julesburg."

"How will we carry the mail?"

"We have had a special saddlebag made for the Pony Express mail called a *mochila*" answered Majors. "It is a wide strip of leather which fits over a very light saddle. The mochila has a pocket in each of the four corners. Three pockets will carry the through mail for California and the fourth will carry the local mail for the stations along the trail."

"When shall I report for duty?"

"Simpson is leaving for Fort Laramie with a wagon train next week. You are to ride with him. You will report to Alf Slade at Julesburg. He is the section boss of the Sweetwater section, and he will give you your orders."

"I will carry out his orders." Bill drew himself up to his full height. "You can count on me, Uncle Alec. Riding for the Pony Express sounds to me as though it will be mighty exciting."

"Yes, but it will be hard work. Two years ago you came to me and asked for a man's job with a wagon train," smiled Majors, "and you proved that you could do a man's job. That's why I am giving you this new job as Pony Express rider." Majors held out his hand. "Remember, Bill, here is a real chance to match yourself with the bravest men of the West. Good-by and good luck. If you see Simpson and McCarthy tell them that I want to see them."

"I'll tell them, Uncle Alec. Thanks again for the job. I'll be in Julesburg by April first and I'll try to be one of the best riders on the Pony Express."

The Boys of the Pony

JULESBURG was located on the South Platte River about four hundred and fifty miles west of Leavenworth. It was a little settlement of about a dozen buildings, but it was one of the largest stations on the overland route used by the Pony Express riders.

Julesburg was the home station for the express riders and stagecoach drivers of this section. The surrounding country was a treeless, barren plain.

The station and stables were long one-story buildings made of cedar logs. The logs had been hauled in by ox teams from a forest a hundred miles farther west. The blacksmith shop and the hay and grain barns were made of adobe, while the little store and other buildings were made of sod.

At one time, robbers and outlaws had overrun the trails near Julesburg. They had held up the stagecoaches carrying gold and money. A number of stagecoach drivers had been killed in the holdups while defending their coaches and passengers.

However, the reckless courage of one man soon made the trails safe. That man, a former stage-coach driver, was Alf Slade. He was a soft-spoken, mild-mannered man with cold, black eyes and the strength of a lion. He was a crack shot and quick on the draw. He was made section boss after he had cleared out the robbers. He was feared by the men who worked for him almost as much as by the outlaws and bandits.

Alf Slade was Bill Cody's new boss.

Simpson's wagon train reached Julesburg late in March. Bill, who had come with Simpson, reported at once to Slade.

"I am Bill Cody," he said. "I am to be one of your Pony Express riders."

"You?" questioned Slade. "You—a Pony Express rider? How old are you?"

"I am fourteen years old, sir, but my age has nothing to do with my job."

"It does on my section," said Slade. "I don't intend to spend my time training boys to carry the mail. I am determined that my riders shall make the best records on the two-thousand-mile trail."

"Then you will need good riders," broke in Bill. "I was hired by Mr. Majors because I am a good rider. He ordered me to report to you."

For a minute Slade hesitated, then he said, "Very well. If Majors hired you, I'll have to give you a chance."

Bill held himself erect. "I'm not asking for a chance to prove to you that I can ride the Pony Express," he said. "I'm telling you that I can do it, and I don't expect any favors from you because Mr. Majors hired me. I can depend upon my own ability."

Slade threw back his head and laughed. "You seem very sure of yourself. By the way, you are wearing a fine brace of revolvers. Are you a good shot?"

Bill nodded. "I am," he answered. "Old Chief Rain-in-the-Face stole my first brace of revolvers, but Mr. McCarthy and Mr. Simpson gave me this pair as a present when Mr. Majors told them that he had hired me as a Pony Express rider."

"Do you mean Frank McCarthy and Lew Simpson, the wagon bosses?"

"Yes, sir, I worked for both of them on their wagon trains."

"That's enough for me, Bill. I know McCarthy and Simpson and I know that anyone who works for them must be good. You may ride with the first mail that reaches my section."

"Thank you, sir."

"Bill," continued Slade, "the Pony Express will start Tuesday, April third. A rider will leave St. Joseph, Missouri, headed west, and on the same day and hour a rider will leave Sacramento, California, headed east. All along the trail other riders are ready to carry the mail through their sections.

"The rider from the east will be the first to reach Julesburg. He is due here Thursday morning. Be ready with your horse to take the mail from him and ride on west with it. You will deliver the mail to the rider who will be waiting for you at the other end of this section."

"I'll be ready," answered Bill.

Bill was up early Thursday morning. He ate

breakfast with Slade and the station agent and then hurried to the stable to saddle Prince.

"Good morning, Bill," called Simpson entering the stable. "This is your big day. Good luck to you."

"Thank you," smiled Bill. "How do you like the new saddle and bridle I have for Prince? All the riders have been given special saddles and bridles. They were made very light so as to keep down the weight that our horses must carry."

"They are light in weight," agreed Simpson, "but they are well made. Doesn't each rider have a mochila to carry the mail?"

"No," answered Bill. "Only one mochila is used on a trip. At each stop it is transferred from horse to horse."

Simpson followed as Bill led Prince to the trail in front of the station. Slade, who had been standing with a group of men, came forward.

"Bill," he said, "you have your orders. Ride! And ride as fast as you can. Let nothing delay you. Do you understand? Nothing!"

"I understand," answered Bill.

"Have you checked your revolvers to see that they are loaded?"

"They are loaded."

"Good, then you are ready?"

"I am ready, sir."

The men laughed and talked as they waited for the rider from the east. Now and then, Slade called to the agent who was standing on the roof of the station, "Do you see anything on the trail?"

"No," the agent would answer, "nothing yet."

Slowly an hour passed. The men became more restless as time dragged on. Bill, however, waited quietly. Slade, watching him, said to himself, "Bill is all right. He will make it."

Suddenly the station agent shouted as he jumped to the ground, "Here he comes! Get ready, Bill!"

In the distance the outline of a galloping horse and its rider came into view. Then came the sound of the horse's hoofbeats pounding over the trail. A few minutes later, the rider pulled his horse to a stop in front of the station and leaped from the saddle.

The station agent was ready. He jerked the

mochila off the panting horse and threw it over
the saddle on Prince. Instantly, Bill was in the
saddle. He leaned low over his horse's neck and
whispered, "Come on, Prince, let's go."

Prince raced like a flash of lightning over the
trail. The men at the station watched as the wind
swept Bill's long golden hair back over his
shoulders. Then horse and rider disappeared over
the top of a small rolling hill.

Slade turned to the men, "That boy can ride!"
He grinned, "And I almost didn't take him."

Prince was a fast horse and Bill did not need to urge him to keep up the swift, steady pace. On and on they sped over the trail. At the first relay station Bill reined in Prince and dismounted. The station agent quickly took the mochila from Prince's saddle and tossed it over the saddle of the fresh horse that stood waiting. As Bill sprang into the saddle of his new mount, Prince whinnied.

"Good-by, old boy," laughed Bill. "I'll get you on my way back. Take good care of my horse," he called to the station agent.

Bill's fresh horse was a sturdy mustang. Like most mustangs he was a wild, spirited animal. He began to buck and prance about, trying to unseat his rider. Bill dug his heels into the mustang's sides and pulled sharply on the reins. "That will be enough of your tricks," he said as the horse broke into a swift gallop. Once again, Bill was on his way.

Bill rode the fifty-mile stretch of his section of the trail in record time. He met stagecoaches on their way to Julesburg, and the drivers and passengers cheered as he raced by. He passed Indian camps and plunged through rushing streams. He waved to a frontier family as he galloped by their lonely cabin. It was the only settler's cabin on his trail.

On his return trip to Julesburg, he carried the mail that had come from California. When he reached the relay station where he had left Prince he found his horse ready. And as Bill jumped into the saddle he felt Prince tremble beneath him.

"Prince, you old rascal," he laughed as they raced away, "I believe you are as excited about carrying the mail as I am."

In less than an hour Bill was in Julesburg and a fresh rider was racing eastward with the mail from California. A few days later, the first through trips between Sacramento and St. Joseph had been completed. The Pony Express was hailed as a great success.

The newspapers of the East carried long exciting articles about the daring riders, how they had crossed the plains and mountains "without danger" from either Indians or outlaws, how they rode the trail both day and night, and how they had brought the mail through, not in ten days, but in nine! "It Is History," read the headline of one great Eastern newspaper. "The Pony Express Is the Fastest Mail System in the World."

These articles also praised Russell, Majors & Waddell for their part in the great undertaking. This praise was justified because the firm had spared no expense in its preparations. Alec Majors insisted that if the first trips could be made without accident or trouble the undertaking would be a success. For this reason, plans for the opening runs were kept secret to prevent Indians or outlaws from attacking riders or stations along the trail.

But how did the people in the West feel about the Pony Express?

The riders were the new heroes of the day. They were affectionately called the Boys of the Pony.

Old plainsmen who had long known the dangers, the hardships, and the loneliness of the unsettled country were their most devoted friends. They considered it an honor to help in any way the Boys of the Pony. And woe to the man who tried to make trouble for them!

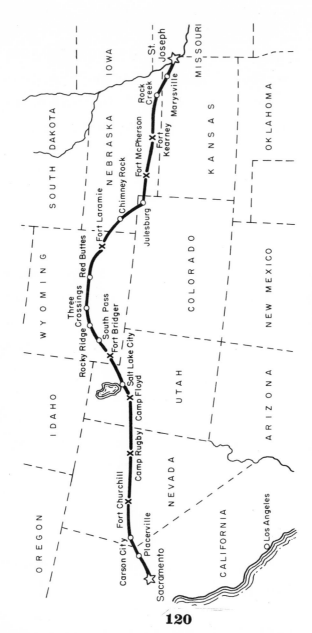

PONY EXPRESS ROUTE

The old plainsmen laughed when told that the newspapers of the East had said the trips were without danger. No dangers? What about the Indians? What would they do when they learned about the Pony Express? Wouldn't they wait in ambush to kill the lonely rider? Wouldn't they try to stop the Pony? Certainly they would.

What about outlaws? Wouldn't they soon begin to hold up the Boys of the Pony?

What about the other dangers of the long, weary miles over wind-swept prairies, the icy mountain trails, and the blazing hot deserts? What about the sudden blizzards, the freezing cold of winter with its sleet and snow? What about the summer heat which parches the earth and dries up the rivers?

No dangers? No hardships?

And very soon, just as the old plainsmen had said, the riders of the Pony Express began to meet the dangers of the trails. Outlaws waylaid them. Indians lurked in ambush along the trail.

But the mail came through! And Bill Cody was one of the Boys of the Pony who helped keep it coming through.

Bill Saves the Mail

ONE DAY the rider from the east was late in reaching Julesburg. Bill, standing by Prince, watched anxiously for a cloud of dust on the trail. On the dry plains the first sign of a rider was the dust kicked up by his galloping horse.

As Bill watched the trail, Prince moved about uneasily as if he were reminding Bill that they should be on their way. Every now and then, the agent came out of the station and looked down the trail toward the east.

"I wonder if he has run into trouble," said Bill as he patted Prince. "He has never been this late before."

The station agent made no reply, but he was worried.

Bill and the other riders of the Pony always waited for one another's arrival with concern. There was a deep feeling of friendship among the

122

boys who shared the dangers and thrills of the Pony. They were quick to praise the daring deeds of their fellow riders, but were modest about their own experiences.

At last the telltale cloud of dust appeared on the trail. Bill turned to the station agent and said, "Here he comes." He tried to act as though he had not been worried.

The station agent laughed. "Bill," he said, "you are just like the rest of the boys. If your rider is late you wait quietly, but you are restless. Then the minute you see him coming you pretend that you have not been worried." He slapped Bill on the back. "I know because that is the way I feel, too."

The rider pulled his horse to a stop in front of the station.

"Is Slade here?" he asked, swinging from the saddle. Quickly the station agent removed the mochila and fitted it over the saddle on Prince.

"No," answered the agent. "He left a week ago for Red Buttes, one of his stations northwest of here. The riders up there are having some Indian trouble and he went up there to settle the trouble."

The rider shook his head. "I wish he were here to settle what Bill should do."

"Why?" asked Bill.

"When I left on this ride, I was told to watch out for Black Marlin, the outlaw. He is waiting somewhere along the trail to rob the Pony," answered the rider.

"That must mean that we are carrying a large sum of money on this trip, doesn't it?" asked Bill.

"Fifty thousand dollars in currency," answered the rider. "I don't know how Marlin found out about it. But someone gave him the tip-off."

"Bill," broke in the station agent, "I don't think you should ride today. Wait until tomorrow. If the Pony doesn't go through today, Marlin will know we have been warned. He will then move on, or lay low for a couple of days."

"He may," said Bill, "but I was hired to carry the mail. Black Marlin is not going to stop me. I am riding today."

"What will you do if you meet the outlaw?"

"I will go prepared to meet him," answered Bill.

"We have an extra mochila in the station, haven't we?" continued Bill.

"Yes," answered the agent. "What are you planning to do?"

Bill grinned. "Marlin is out to get a mochila and I am going to get one ready for him."

He ran into the station. The agent and the other rider followed him.

The agent gave Bill the extra mochila. Bill explained his plan as he filled the pockets of the mochila with paper. The pockets looked as though they were full of mail or money. As Bill locked the pockets he asked, "Why were you late today?"

"Indians," answered the rider. "Luckily I met a stagecoach and the driver warned me to look out for Indians ahead. To avoid them I left the trail and rode about ten miles out of my way."

"Did the driver tell you what Indians were on the trail?" asked Bill.

"Yes, Yellow Hand and his Cheyenne braves."

"Yellow Hand!" exclaimed Bill. "That horse thief!"

"Bill," laughed the rider, "don't tell me again

how Yellow Hand stole Prince and how Kit Carson got your horse back for you."

"I am not thinking of Prince this time," said Bill. "I am thinking of how much trouble Yellow Hand can make for the Boys of the Pony. He is a tricky and dangerous enemy. Now that he is on the trail again we are liable to have a run-in with him any time. Watch out for him."

Bill picked up the mochila and hurried back to Prince. Quickly he removed the mochila with the money and the mail. Then he removed the saddle and the saddle blanket. Carefully he placed the mochila with the money on Prince's back and then covered it with the saddle blanket. Next he saddled Prince and threw the mochila with the paper in its pockets over the saddle.

"I still think you should wait until tomorrow, Bill," said the station agent. "You are riding straight into trouble and you may be killed."

"I know that I am taking a risk," said Bill, "but if my plan works, the mail goes through."

Bill sprang into the saddle and called, "Come on, Prince. Let's go. We're late."

"Good luck, Bill," called the rider and the station agent as Prince sped away.

Bill rode swiftly, but he watched the trail carefully for signs of the outlaws or Indians. The endless stretch of plain was broken only by the sandy hills in the distance. And the only sounds were those of Prince's pounding hoofbeats on the rough trail.

"If I can get through the narrow pass ahead of me where the trail runs between two hills, I can make the first relay station," he said to himself. "That is the one place on this ride that an outlaw or Indian would pick for a holdup."

When they neared the hills, Bill leaned flat against Prince's neck. "Come on, old boy!" he cried.

Just as Prince reached the hills, two masked men stepped out on the trail. Both outlaws held their rifles ready to fire. They blocked the narrow pass completely.

Bill pulled Prince to a stop.

"Reach for the sky!" commanded one of the outlaws firmly.

Without a word, Bill raised his hands above his head.

"Get down!" ordered the outlaw, "but keep your hands up."

Bill hesitated. He said to himself, "If I seem too willing to let them take the mochila they may become suspicious; and if I make a wrong move they may shoot me."

"Hit the dirt!" repeated the outlaw.

"Is this a holdup?" asked Bill.

"What do you think?" sneered the second outlaw. "Get off your horse and give us that mochila."

"Let me handle this," snapped the first outlaw. "Son," he said turning to Bill, "stop wasting our time. Give me the mochila and I will let you go."

"But I can't," protested Bill. "The mochila is carrying United States mail."

"And fifty thousand dollars," added the outlaw.

"Are you Black Marlin?" asked Bill.

The outlaw nodded.

"Robbing the United States mail is a serious crime," said Bill, jumping to the ground. "Sooner or later the government will catch you."

"Let me worry about that," laughed Marlin.

"All right." Bill began to remove the mochila. He said to himself, "I must get away before they open the mochila and find out that I have tricked them." Aloud he said, "Of course you know I will report this robbery."

"Sure, but by that time we will be gone," smiled Marlin. "You are a plucky youngster. I like your nerve. You don't seem to be the least bit afraid."

"I'm not." Bill snatched the mochila from the saddle, turned quickly, and flung it with all his might straight at Marlin's head.

The sudden move startled the outlaws who no longer had Bill covered with their rifles. Stepping back out of the way, Marlin stumbled over a rock and fell to the ground. The other outlaw leaned over to pick up the mochila. In that instant Bill whipped out his revolver.

"Drop your guns and back away," he ordered.

Still keeping his revolver trained on them Bill mounted his horse. He touched Prince with his spurs.

Before the robbers could recover their rifles,

Bill was galloping rapidly away toward the west.

"When they open the mochila they will come after me," he said to himself as he urged Prince to greater speed.

He looked back over his shoulder. The outlaws were opening the mochila. Suddenly one of them reached for his rifle, took quick aim, and fired. The bullet whistled past Bill's head. Several more shots were fired, but they all went wild. In another few seconds, Bill was out of their range.

Bill dashed into the relay station on time. "Black Marlin is on the trail!" he called.

"And he robbed the Pony!" exclaimed the agent as Bill removed Prince's saddle.

"No, he didn't." Bill pulled back the saddle blanket. "The mail is safe. I thought my plan would work, and it did. But," he added, and he laughed a little, "I wasn't really sure until I was out of their rifle range."

"Another dangerous ride made by a Boy of the Pony!" praised the agent. "Good for you, Bill."

Trouble on the Sweetwater

DAY BY DAY the dangers faced by the Boys of the Pony increased. Outlaws made many bold attempts to hold up the riders. Indians on the warpath swept down in surprise attacks upon the small relay stations and burned them to the ground. They killed and scalped the agents. They stole supplies and drove off the horses. But the Pony Express continued to carry the mail through safely and on time.

Late one night Bill returned to Julesburg after his day's run. He cared for Prince before he went to the station to eat his supper. He was tired and he walked slowly up the path from the stables to the open door of the station. He paused outside as the sound of voices came from within.

"I tell you the run from Red Buttes to Three Crossings is too dangerous for the boy," came the station agent's voice through the darkness.

"Slade doesn't seem to think so," said the voice of another man.

"Doesn't Slade have enough riders up there?" asked the agent.

"Yes," answered the man, "but he is having a lot of trouble with the Indians and outlaws and he has decided to put his best riders on that run. That is why he wants Bill Cody transferred to Red Buttes. Bill must be good if Slade wants him to ride one of the roughest, toughest runs on the two-thousand-mile trail."

"He is good!" exclaimed the agent. "I'm sorry to lose him."

"Maybe he won't go. Slade said to let Bill decide after I had told him of the dangers of this run."

"You don't know Bill Cody," interrupted the agent. "The more danger on the job the better he likes it."

"You are right," laughed Bill as he entered the station. "When do I report to Slade?"

The men looked at each other and laughed.

Bill lost no time in reporting for duty on his new job. Slade was glad to see him.

"I knew you would come," said Slade as he greeted Bill. "Now here are your orders. You are to carry the mail from Red Buttes to Three Crossings, seventy-six miles west of here, and then make your return trip with the mail from California. You will be paid one hundred and fifty dollars a month on this run."

"Good!" exclaimed Bill. "That's the top pay for a rider!"

"That's true," laughed Slade, "and for a very good reason. This is a tough run, Bill, and you will earn every cent of it. The trail is difficult and it is through the heart of the Indian country. You will also have to be on the lookout for bandits. You must be careful, but I still expect you to get the mail through on time."

"I'll do my best, sir."

"Your word is all I need," replied Slade. "Be ready to ride in the morning."

Bill's new route was, as Slade had said, a difficult one. The trail was rough and uneven. It was over a barren sandy plain broken by towering buttes, or hills. The sagebrush which grew along the trail and dotted the plains made a perfect ambush for Indians and outlaws.

In the morning, Bill, mounted on Prince, was on the trail to Three Crossings. As always, he rode his own horse to the first relay station. Bill had come to depend upon Prince's speed to make a good start on each trip. If Bill was late on a return trip it was Prince who made up the lost time and raced into the home station on time.

On this first trip over the new route, Bill's quick eyes and alert mind took in every detail. He must become familiar with every inch of the trail so that he could ride it even on the darkest night.

Near Three Crossings, the trail became even more difficult. It followed along the bank of the twisting, turning Sweetwater River which ran through a canyon. Three times within a few rods the trail disappeared into the rushing waters and appeared again on the opposite bank.

"Three Crossings," Bill laughed to himself. "It is not very hard to understand how this station got its name." After the third crossing, he gave his horse the spurs.

As Bill's horse galloped up to the little station at the end of his route, the rider from the west arrived. The station agent was waiting with two fresh horses.

"Bob!" exclaimed Bill as the rider dismounted. "I am glad to see you."

"Bill Cody! I am glad to see you, too. I was told that the new rider on this run was a friend of mine, but I didn't know that you had been transferred to Red Buttes."

"This is my first ride on this run."

"Did you have any trouble?" asked Bob.

"No," answered Bill, "not this time. How long a run do you make, Bob?"

"Eighty-five miles west of here to Rocky Ridge."

The station agent exchanged the mochilas and the boys mounted their fresh horses.

"Good-by, Bob," called Bill over his shoulder as he swung onto his horse and started away on his return trip toward the east. "See you on the next run."

"Good luck, Bill," called Bob as his horse raced away toward the west.

Twice a week for three weeks Bill and Bob met at Three Crossings with the mail. They looked forward to their short visits. They laughed and talked of the experiences they had shared when they rode cavayard together with the wagon trains.

Whenever Bob arrived at Three Crossings before Bill, he watched for Bill's arrival. If Bill reached the station ahead of Bob, he anxiously watched the western trail for his friend. The kindly station agent was always ready with fresh horses and a cheery greeting for the boys.

But one day, as Bill neared the station, the agent was not waiting with the horses.

"Yip! Yip! Yipee" Bill shouted a warning call. There was no answer.

"Yip! Yip!" he called again.

He pulled his horse to a stop in front of the station and dismounted.

Bill ran to the station and threw open the door. He stepped back and his sun-tanned face paled.

There, lying face down on the floor with an arrow through his body, was the station agent. Beside him lay another man in a pool of blood, with a feathered arrow through his heart.

"Bob!" cried Bill. He dropped to one knee beside his dead friend. In Bob's hands was the mochila which Bill was to take back east to Red Buttes. In death, Bob, a Boy of the Pony, was still faithful to his trust. The mail was safe.

For a minute Bill did not move. Then suddenly he jumped to his feet. He removed the arrows from the two still figures. He examined the arrows closely.

"Cheyenne arrows," he said to himself as he broke them into pieces. "This could be some of Yellow Hand's work."

He leaned over and took the mochila from Bob's dead hands. "Bob," he promised, "I'll get your mail back to your station, and I'll get it there as you always have done—on time."

Bill ran to the corral. The gate was open and all the horses were gone. He did not hesitate. He threw both mochilas over the saddle of his weary horse and mounted. Instead of heading back to Red Buttes he rode westward over the trail of his dead friend.

"I hate to do this to you, old boy," he said to the horse, "but we must go on to the next station."

When Bill reached the first relay station he reported the murders to the station agent in charge.

"We have been expecting trouble," said the agent. "A man came in on the last stagecoach to help me for a few days. I'll send him with some horses to Three Crossings to take charge of the station until Slade can get another agent."

"I'll leave Bob's mochila here with you. It is filled with mail for the East. I'll pick it up later on my way back to Red Buttes."

Without stopping to rest, Bill mounted a fresh horse and dashed on over the westward trail.

Darkness fell. On over the unfamiliar trail Bill raced with the mail. He stopped at each station only long enough to change horses. At last he reached Rocky Ridge, the end of Bob's run.

"Hello, Bob," called the waiting agent as Bill's horse thundered up to the station. "You are on time."

"I am not Bob," said Bill swinging from his saddle. "I am Bill Cody. Bob was killed at Three

Crossings this afternoon by some Cheyennes. He was a friend of mine and I brought the mail through for him."

"Glad to meet you, Bill. That's bad news about Bob. Sorry to hear it. Come in, come in. You must spend the night here."

"No, I must leave as soon as I can get a fresh horse. I must get my own mochila back to Red Buttes."

"Red Buttes!" exclaimed the station agent, "that is one hundred and sixty miles from here."

"I know it," said Bill, "but I must make my return trip tonight."

"You must get some rest," protested the agent. "You can't ride over three hundred miles without time out to rest or eat."

"I must leave at once," said Bill. "Please bring me a fresh horse."

"Very well. Come with me into the station and I'll give this mochila to the rider for the west. Then I'll get a horse ready for you."

Bill followed the agent into the station. "Here's Bill Cody," he said to a group of men. "Bob was murdered by the Cheyennes and Bill brought the mail through for his friend. That's the kind of loyalty that keeps the Pony going."

The men crowded around Bill. They asked him many questions. However, one man, a tall powerful man with blond curly hair, remained silent. His clothes were expensive and his black, polished boots were of fine leather. He wore a brace of pearl-handled revolvers around his slim waist.

Everything about this man made him seem out of place among the roughly dressed men of the plains. But there was a look of cold courage in the man's gray-blue eyes that commanded respect. And there was a quiet self-confidence in his manner that marked him as a leader among men.

"I wonder who he is," Bill said to himself.

The station agent handed the man a letter. As the man read it he frowned. He looked up from the letter and motioned to Bill. "Come here, Bill," he said, "I want you to do something for me."

"Yes, sir," said Bill as he stood before him.

"I am Bill Hickok," said the man.

"Bill Hickok?"

"Yes," smiled Hickok, "and I have a message for your boss, Alf Slade. Tell him that Majors has ordered me to help him clear out the Indians and bandits on the Sweetwater section. I will report to him next Thursday at Red Buttes. Tell him to have a posse of forty men ready for me."

"Yes, sir."

"That is all," said Hickok. "Good luck to you on your ride back to Red Buttes."

"Thank you, sir."

"Bill Cody, your horse is ready," called the station agent.

As Bill joined the agent he asked, "Is Mr. Hickok the same man as Wild Bill Hickok?"

"That's right. You have just met the famous Wild Bill Hickok."

"But he doesn't look like a real plainsman."

"Don't let those blond curls and quiet manners fool you, son. Wild Bill Hickok is one of the most fearless men in the West. He is an Indian fighter, scout, stagecoach driver, and a terror to outlaws. Wild Bill is a loyal friend but an enemy to be avoided."

Bill mounted the waiting horse and started on his return trip to Red Buttes. He rode swiftly and made his stations in good time. The relief agent had already taken over at Three Crossings and Bill was given a fresh horse when he reached the station.

On over the difficult trail the weary boy rode toward Red Buttes. His body ached and his eyes were heavy with sleep.

But at last he reached the end of the long ride. He had ridden three hundred and twenty-two miles in twenty-one hours and forty minutes.

"Bill, you crazy kid!" said Slade after Bill had reported to him. "You've made a record ride that the Pony will never forget. Now get some sleep and I'll talk to you about Wild Bill Hickok later."

*   *   *

Bill Cody's ride is the longest continuous horseback ride in history. This record still stands unbroken, and it was made by a boy of fourteen who was determined that he would not fail the Boys of the Pony.

Wild Bill Hickok

WILD BILL Hickok arrived at Red Buttes early Thursday morning. As Hickok reined in his horse and swung from the saddle, Slade hurried out of the station to meet him.

"Wild Bill," he said shaking hands with the famous plainsman, "I am glad to see you."

"And I am glad to see you, Slade," said Hickok. "Majors sent me to help you clear out the Indians and outlaws on your section. But I still feel that you could do this job yourself."

"I can't fight Indians, hunt down outlaws, and keep my riders on the job all at the same time," laughed Slade. "I certainly need your help. What are your plans?"

"Well, as you know, the Pony has been stopped," answered Hickok. "No more mail will be carried until we can make the trails safe for the riders. I think the first thing we should do is to get the horses the Indians have stolen from the Pony. Don't you think so?"

"Yes, I do," answered Slade quickly.

"Then we should run down the outlaws who have been holding up the riders on your section," continued Hickok. "The surest way of capturing them is to locate their hideout. Do you agree?"

"I certainly do."

"Good! By the way, I saw one of your riders in Rocky Ridge. Bill Cody was his name."

"Yes, I know," answered Slade.

"He said that he was going to make the return trip that night. Did he do it?'

Slade threw back his head and laughed. "Did he? He certainly did. Hickok, that boy is the best rider on my section. He gave me your message and I have the forty men ready for you. Bill Cody wants to go with us. I told him that as far as, I am concerned he could go, but that you were in charge and that I would ask you. What about it?"

"You think he's all right, don't you?"

"He is young, but I wish I had forty men just like him." Slade pointed toward the corral. "See there, he is giving his horse, Prince, a good rub-down. He is crazy about that horse."

"Bill Cody," called Hickok, "you better get ready if you want to ride with us. We are going to get the stolen horses from the Indians."

A short time later, the posse of forty mounted men left the station. Bill, riding Prince, was in front with Hickok and Slade. The posse traveled rapidly over the trail toward the Sweetwater River. When they came to the river Hickok ordered a halt.

"We will divide into two parties," he said. "You ten men," and he pointed to the men, "are to ride with me and scout the country for signs of the Indians. Slade, you and the rest of the men keep to the trail. I'll take Bill Cody with me and if we locate the Indians, I will send him back to let you know."

Hickok and his scouts rode on. They spread out to look for signs of the Indians. Bill, leaning over Prince's neck, carefully watched the ground. Hickok looked for Indian signs as he rode along, but he also kept a close watch on Bill.

When they had ridden about twenty miles, Bill suddenly reined in Prince and dismounted. Prince stood quietly as his master crawled along the ground on his hands and knees.

Hickok signaled to his scouts and gave his horse the spurs. The men galloped toward Bill.

"What have you found, Bill?" asked Hickok as he pulled up beside the boy.

"I think I have located the Indians' trail." answered Bill. "See, here are the hoofprints of their unshod ponies. And here are the hoofprints of the horses that are shod. The horses that are shod don't belong to the Indians. They are horses that were stolen from the Pony."

Hickok slipped from his saddle and knelt on the ground. He examined the tracks.

"You are right, Bill. The Indians are leading our horses. Notice that the hoofprints of the shod horses are more distinct and are on top of the hoofprints of the unshod ponies. Ride back to Slade and lead him to this trail. My scouts and I will ride on to the north. When you return with Slade and his men, pick up our trail and follow us."

Hickok and his scouts followed the trail all day but did not overtake the Indians. Late the next afternoon they located the Indian camp near a small creek. There were about three hundred braves in camp. A hundred stolen horses were grazing nearby. Hickok watched the Indians for a while. Then he and his scouts hurried back to meet Slade and his men.

"The Indians don't suspect that we are on their trail," said Hickok. "They have no guards posted. We are outnumbered, but we will make a surprise attack as soon as it is dark. When I give the signal we will charge straight through the camp. Ride hard, keep together, and shoot to kill."

The Indians were taken by surprise. Hickok, with a blazing revolver in each hand, led the attack. The men raced through the camp yelling and shooting. They made so much noise and confusion that the Indians, thinking they were outnumbered, fled into the darkness.

In the morning five men were ordered to round up the horses and take them to the nearest Pony Express station.

"Bill," asked Hickok as he turned and winked at Slade, "don't you want to help take the horses to the station?"

"No, sir," answered Bill quickly. "I want to help locate the outlaws. Of course," he added, "if you order me to go, I will go, but I won't like it."

Hickok laughed. Then he asked, and his voice was kindly, "Why are you so anxious to go with the posse? You don't need to go."

"Well, you see, sir," said Bill, "I expect to be a scout some day and I need all the experience I can get so I will be a good one."

Hickok slapped Bill on the shoulder. "Good boy," he said and strode away.

Hickok and his men scouted the country for many days. They explored the canyons and followed trails over the hills and mountains. But they found no signs of the outlaws.

Every day the men spent long, weary hours in the saddle. Every night they made camp wherever they happened to be when it became dark. They built no campfires because they did not want to attract the attention of roving bands of Indians, or of outlaws in case their hideout should be near the posse's camp. They ate cold meat and dry bread and slept on the ground.

One night, camp was made just inside the entrance to a large canyon. The horses were watered at the little creek flowing through the canyon and then were hobbled nearby. The men talked in low voices as they ate their supper.

"Slade," said Hickok, "tomorrow morning we will explore this canyon. You and your men follow the creek. My scouts and I will take the trail to the top of the canyon."

"All right. I'll do that," said Slade. "Shall we meet you at the other end of the canyon or shall we meet back here?"

"Meet me at the other end," answered Hickok, "we must keep moving forward."

After talking over the plans for the next morning, Hickok said, "Well, I guess I'll turn in for the night. Bill, what about you?"

"I'll be ready as soon as I hobble Prince for the night."

"Why don't you hobble your horse when we

make camp?" asked Hickok. "It would save you a lot of trouble each night. He always roams away from camp."

Bill laughed. "He never goes very far and he always comes back when I call him."

Prince had wandered a short distance up the canyon. But when Bill called softly to him the horse started at once toward his master. They made their way through the darkness back to camp.

Suddenly Bill stopped. "What was that I saw reflected on the canyon wall?" he asked himself. He stood perfectly still. He stared intently at the distant canyon wall.

Far up the canyon was a faint glow of light.

"It's a campfire!" he exclaimed. "Come, Prince," he added.

He led Prince quickly back to the other horses and hobbled him. "Stay here, old fellow," he said. "I won't need you on this job."

He hurried back to camp.

"Mr. Hickok," he called in a loud whisper.

"What's the matter, Bill? Has someone stolen Prince?"

"No," answered Bill, "but I believe I've located the hideout of the outlaws."

Quick as a flash Hickok sprang to his feet.

"What makes you think so, Bill?" called Slade.

"I was leading Prince back toward camp when I saw a faint glow of light reflected against the side of this canyon wall. Look off to the right. See! There it is. It is a campfire!"

"You are right, Bill," said Hickok.

"Could be some campers," said one of the men.

"No one but an outlaw gang would be camped way up there in that out-of-the-way place. They think they are safe or they wouldn't have a campfire," said Hickok.

"Let's find out who it is," said Slade. "What are we waiting for?"

"I'll take Bill with me and go up the canyon," said Hickok. "If we find that it is the outlaws' camp, I'll send word back by Bill. Slade, I'll depend upon you and the men to be ready to follow Bill in case he brings you word that we are to try to capture the outlaws tonight. Get your guns, Bill, and come with me."

Hickok and Bill left camp at once. They moved cautiously and quietly over the rough canyon path. In a short time, they struck a narrow trail that entered the canyon from the right. A little farther on they came to a place where the trail divided.

"You take the path to the right and I'll keep on straight ahead," said Hickok in a low voice. "Go about a half mile up the canyon and then come back and report to me here. If I am not here, wait for me."

"Yes, sir."

Bill went on alone. Slowly, carefully he made his way through the darkness. Now and then, he paused and listened. Not a sound broke the stillness of the night. The path became narrower. The light on ahead became brighter. He dropped to his hands and knees and crawled on up the rocky path.

Suddenly a gruff voice demanded, "Who is it?"

Bill did not answer.

"Who is it?"

Bill said to himself, "A guard! I'm in for it now. I must act fast to get out of this." He rose to his feet and said, "I am looking for a camping place."

"You have come a long way in the dark to find a camping place."

"I am lost," said Bill.

"Stand where you are. Make one move and I'll fill you full of lead," said the guard. Slowly the man came down the narrow path.

Bill backed up against the canyon wall. The man brushed past him. Bill hesitated for just an instant and then struck with all his might. There was a grunt and the man toppled over the edge of the path and fell into the canyon below.

"This path leads to the outlaws' hideout," said Bill to himself. "I must get back to Mr. Hickok and tell him what has happened." He moved quickly and quietly down the path.

Hickok was waiting. In a few words Bill told him about the guard and what had happened.

"Good work, Bill," praised Hickok. "Now get back to camp and bring Slade and the men. I'll wait here and see that no one gets by this spot."

A little later Bill and the posse, headed by Slade,

joined Hickok. Then with Bill in the lead the men made their way quietly up the narrow path.

"This is where I met the guard," whispered Bill.

"All right. Step back, Bill," said Hickok. "From now on I'll lead the way."

Slowly they made their way along the trail. As Hickok and his men crept around a large rock, the outlaws' campfire came into view. Twelve rough men, armed with rifles, were gathered around the fire. They were laughing and talking.

Hickok halted his men. "You know what to do," he said. "Move into position around the camp. When I cover the outlaws, close in."

Without a word the men obeyed.

After waiting long enough for his men to surround the camp, Hickok whipped out his pearl-handled revolvers and strode forward.

"Hands up!" he commanded.

The outlaws jumped to their feet.

"Get him!" shouted one of them as he reached for his rifle. Hickok's revolvers barked and the outlaw fell dead.

The posse surrounding the outlaws closed in. The bandits made no attempt to shoot their way out of the circle of guns held ready to fire.

"Throw your guns on the ground!" ordered Hickok. "Who's the leader of this gang?"

"I am," growled one of the outlaws.

"Black Marlin!" exclaimed Bill.

The outlaw turned and glared. "Oh, you're the Kid of the Pony. I remember you. I'll get you one of these days."

"Come on, men," broke in Hickok, "get the

ropes over there by the fire and tie up these bandits. We had a tough time locating them and we don't want to take a chance on losing them."

"How did you find our hideout?" snarled Marlin.

"You're getting careless, Marlin," laughed Hickok. "My scout, that Kid of the Pony, spotted your campfire and the rest was easy."

––––––––––

The flag of the Postmaster General of the United States bears a design of the Pony Express rider. It is a fitting tribute to the courage, endurance, and honor of the Boys of the Pony.

Last Days of the Pony

A FEW days after the capture of the outlaws, the Pony Express began to carry the mail again. The outlaws were on their way to stand trial for their crimes.

Hickok and his men continued to scout the trails for signs of Indians. But they found that the Indians were staying near their villages or camps far from the Pony trail. Hickok was ordered to move on to another section farther west to help round up another band of outlaws. He said good-by to Slade, Bill, and the men of the Red Buttes station and rode away.

When the gangs of outlaws had been broken up, the Indians and outlaws did not molest the Pony for several months. Back and forth over the trail the boys raced their speedy horses. The nine-day mail service was shortened to eight days.

Then once again, bandits came out of hiding and

began to waylay the Boys of the Pony. Indians began to lurk along the trail. Once again the stations were burned, agents were killed, and horses and supplies were stolen. But this time the Pony was not stopped. The boys, more determined than ever, made their rides and, in spite of all dangers, brought the mail through on time.

On October 24, 1861, the telegraph line connecting the West and the East was completed. Now important messages could be flashed across the continent in a few minutes. The Pony was no longer needed. It had served its purpose.

The Pony had lasted only eighteen months. The Boys of the Pony had not only carried the mail, but they had made history. The record of their reckless deeds and daring rides is one of the most thrilling chapters in the history of our country. The story of the Pony cannot be told without including the exciting adventures of the Kid of the Pony, Bill Cody.

As soon as Bill finished his last ride with the mail, he left Red Buttes and returned to Leavenworth. After a short visit with his mother and sisters, he went to see his friend, Alec Majors.

"I am glad to see you, Bill," said Majors. He pointed to a chair. "Sit down. I suppose you have come to see me about a new job."

"Yes, Uncle Alec."

"I am afraid that this time I can't give you one," Majors shook his head. "The firm of Russell, Majors & Waddell is going out of business. My partners and I have lost all our money. Once I was a wealthy man, but during the past eighteen months I have lost more than a million dollars. All I have left now is my home and a few thousand dollars."

"Uncle Alec, what happened?"

"My partners and I knew almost from the start of the Pony Express that we would lose money. But we had a contract to carry out and we lost our entire fortunes doing it. That's all, Bill."

"I can't believe it, Uncle Alec. I thought the Pony was a success."

"Our firm failed, but that does not mean that the Pony failed, Bill. The Pony was a success. I have spent my life on the plains and I will always believe that the Pony was the biggest and finest service we could have done for our country. If I were to be given another chance to choose between the Pony and my fortune I would not hesitate. The Pony would win."

"I don't know what to say, Uncle Alec. But I think you are a great man."

Majors smiled. "I'm not a great man, Bill. Let us say instead that I am a man who loves the West."

They were silent for a moment. Then Bill asked, "What will you do, Uncle Alec? Can I help you?"

"First of all, the business affairs of the firm must be settled. We are selling our stagecoach line to Ben Holladay. Then I intend to do what I did as a young man. I started out with one wagon train carrying freight across the plains. And that is what I will do again."

"Let me work with your wagon train," broke in Bill. "I will ride cavayard for you, or I will drive a wagon, or scout. I will do anything to help you, Uncle Alec."

"I know you would, Bill," smiled Majors, "and I am grateful to you. Simpson and McCarthy were here today and they both want a job with my train. In fact all my men have offered to help me. I am very proud that I have so many loyal friends. But I am not ready to start my wagon train now. It may take several months to settle the business affairs of the firm. Until that is done, I cannot be certain of my own plans for the future."

A little later, Bill said good-by to Majors and left the office. He stood for a minute outside the closed door. "Uncle Alec is right," he said to himself. "He is a man who loves the West. I understand more clearly now how much the future of the West depends upon the courage, faith, and honor of such men. Uncle Alec, you have taught me how important it is for each man to do his share in this great work. I will try to continue to do my part."

He hurried from the building, mounted Prince, and headed for home.

Bill was glad to be home with his mother and sisters. However, he was worried about his mother. Mrs. Cody had been ill for several months. She was pale and thin. She insisted that she had recovered from her former illness, but the Cody children realized that their mother was never going to be well again. Their gentle little mother who had always been so active was to spend the rest of her life as an invalid.

Bill's sisters were heartsick and bewildered. They turned to him for courage and comfort. And although he was sick with worry over his mother's illness, he did not let them know it.

"We must not let Mother worry about anything," he said to them. "I will get another job as soon as I can. Mother is to have everything she needs to make her happy."

Bill went again to Majors' office. He told his old friend of his mother's ill health. "I need a job at once," he said. "Will you give me a letter of recommendation?"

"Yes, but you don't need it. You can go anywhere and ask any man for a job and get it. Your name, Bill Cody, is better than any letter of recommendation."

"Thank you, Uncle Alec."

"What do you want to do this time?"

"I want to be a scout for wagon trains going west

from Leavenworth," answered Bill. "A job of this kind would enable me to see my mother from time to time."

"Bill, this is a serious time in our country's history. The war between the states has taken most of our good scouts away from the plains. They have joined either the Confederate or the Union Army. And now there is some talk of an Indian uprising. The government is anxious to keep the western forts supplied and to protect the settlers. If I were you I would get a job as scout with a wagon train carrying government supplies to these forts. You can see your mother each time you return to Leavenworth."

"I will do that, Uncle Alec."

And for the next two years Bill was a scout with the wagon trains hauling government supplies. He was a fearless scout. He was alert and cautious, for the lives of many men depended upon him. He soon came to be regarded as one of the safest and best wagon train scouts on the plains.

A few days before Christmas in 1863, Bill returned to Leavenworth after a long, hard trip with a wagon train. He stopped in the little town, gay with Christmas cheer, only long enough to buy some gifts for his mother and sisters. Then with a happy heart he hurried to his cabin home. He had great plans for a merry Christmas with his family.

But his home-coming was soon filled with sorrow. Mrs. Cody was dangerously ill.

Bill knelt beside her bed. "Mother," he said quietly, "I am home."

"Billy, Billy." Mrs. Cody opened her eyes. "Oh, Billy," she smiled, "I knew you would be home for Christmas. I feel better already."

"Of course you do, Mother."

But in spite of everything the doctor could do, Mrs. Cody died in her sleep late that night.

Romance

ONE DAY in January, Bill mounted Prince and rode to the house of a nearby farmer. As Bill turned his horse in at the gate, the farmer's ten-year-old son ran to meet him.

"Hello, Bill," called the boy.

"Hello, there," called Bill in answer. "Is your father at home?"

"Yes, he is."

"Good!" Bill dismounted and followed the boy into the house.

"Father, Bill Cody wants to see you."

"What is it, Bill?" asked the farmer. "What can I do for you?"

"I have enlisted in the Union Army," answered Bill, "and I must find a home for Prince before I leave to join my troop. Will you take care of him for me?"

"What about it, Son?" asked the farmer. "Do

you want to take care of Bill Cody's horse while he is in the army?"

"Oh, yes," answered the boy. "I would be glad to take care of Prince."

"Prince needs a good home for the rest of his life," said Bill.

"I would be glad to buy him for my son," broke in the farmer. "He thinks that Prince is the finest horse in the world. How much do you want for him?"

Bill shook his head. "I couldn't sell Prince. He and I have had too many adventures together." He turned to the boy. "But if you will take good care of him—" he hesitated —"I will give Prince to you."

"You mean that if I take good care of him that I may have Prince for my own?" questioned the boy.

"Yes," smiled Bill. "I want someone who will be good to Prince to have him."

"Oh, I'll take good care of Prince," promised the boy.

"Then he is yours," said Bill. "I know that you and Prince will have fine times together."

Bill said good-by to the farmer, and he and the boy left the house. They went to where Prince was standing. Bill put his arms around the horse's neck. "Good-by, old boy," he whispered. "You have been a great pal. I will never forget you— my old Prince of the Pony."

Then without another word he hurried away.

Bill Cody left Leavenworth and joined his troop. He served in the Union Army until the end of the war. Because of his experience as a scout on the western plains, he was soon made a scout in the army. He carried out his orders faithfully and won the respect of his superior officers.

Just before the war ended, he was stationed in St. Louis, Missouri. It was the first time he had ever been in a large city. Although he enjoyed the interesting old city, he missed the exciting life on the plains.

Whenever he had time off from his duties in the army, he went to a park and rode horseback over its shady paths. But he longed for the endless western trails and the vast rolling plains.

"This city is all right," he would say to himself,

"but this is not home. I guess I'll never feel at home in a city."

Several times, as he rode through the park, he passed a young lady riding a spirited horse. She was very beautiful and best of all she was a good rider.

One afternoon when Bill was riding in the park, the young lady rode past him. Her horse was prancing nervously. Suddenly the horse shied, reared into the air, and plunged forward. The young lady pulled sharply on the reins but could not control the frightened animal. Her horse broke into a gallop and raced away.

Bill gave his horse the spurs. Quickly he began to gain on the runaway horse. Soon he pulled up alongside the frightened animal and grabbed the bridle. He brought the horse to a stop and jumped to the ground.

"Are you all right?" he asked looking up into the young lady's pale face.

"Yes," she laughed, but her voice trembled. "Please help me dismount," she added. "I feel as though I am going to faint."

Bill helped the young lady dismount. She rested for a few minutes and then she asked, "Will you take me to my home? I am Louisa Frederici."

"Of course I will take you home. I am Bill Cody."

Leading both horses, Bill walked with Louisa to her home.

Her father and mother thanked Bill for rescuing their daughter. They invited him to stay for dinner that evening, and he accepted the invitation.

From that time until the end of Bill's stay in St. Louis, he and Louisa spent much of their time together. They rode through the parks. They walked along the shady streets in the old French quarter of the city where Louisa lived. They spent the evening hours in the little French garden of the Frederici home. They laughed, and sang, and were happy. They were in love.

At last the war was over, and Bill was discharged from the army. He asked Louisa to marry him, and her answer was, "Yes."

"Then I must return to the West and get a job," said Bill. "As soon as I have earned enough money,

I'll come back to St. Louis and we will be married."

"Can't you get a job in St. Louis?"

Bill was silent for a minute. "The West is my home," he began in a low voice, "and out on the plains I know that I can always make a living. But it is more than that, Louisa. It is the part of the country that I understand and love. I want to do my share in building the West.

"I can't give you a life of comfort, or of wealth, such as you have now," he went on, "but, Louisa, I shall try to make you happy, and I believe that you will learn to love the West."

"I will wait for you here," smiled Louisa, "and then, somewhere in the West, we will find happiness together."

"I will go back to Leavenworth," said Bill. "I will get a job at once."

"What will you do?"

"I don't know, Louisa, but there is always something I can do. I may drive a stagecoach, or scout for a wagon train."

Bill said good-by to Louisa and took a river steamboat up the Missouri River to Leavenworth.

He went at once to Alec Majors' old office.

"Majors has gone west with his wagon train," said the man seated at Majors' desk. "But if you are looking for a job maybe I can help you. I am Ben Holladay."

"I'm Bill Cody."

Holladay threw back his head and laughed. "Well, I'm not so sure that I can help you but you certainly can help me. I'd like to sign you up as one of my stagecoach drivers. How about it?"

"I'd like nothing better," answered Bill.

"Good! When can you begin working for me?"

"I want to spend a few days with my sisters," replied Bill, "then I'll be ready to drive whenever you need me."

"Your run will be from Fort Kearney to Plum Creek. Report to the agent at Fort Kearney for further orders."

"I'll do that, sir," Bill left the office and as he closed the door, Holladay said to himself, "Watch out, you stagecoach drivers—here comes Bill Cody."

A Knight of the Reins

BILL CODY visited his sisters for a few days. Then he left his old home to begin work on his new job. He reported to the agent in charge of the Holladay stagecoach station at Fort Kearney. The agent had already been notified that Bill was to drive for the Holladay line.

The Ben Holladay stagecoach lines were the longest and best-equipped lines, not only in the West, but in the world. Their coaches, loaded with passengers, express, gold, and mail traveled over more than five thousand miles of western trails. One of the most important lines operated by Holladay was over the old Pony Express Trail.

It had cost a large sum of money to equip the lines. One hundred stagecoaches and nearly three thousand mules and horses had been bought. Holladay had spared no expense. He had bought the finest coaches and the best animals and harness for

173

the teams. He had hired the best drivers and the most fearless men as division agents. To operate the lines cost several million dollars each year.

"Cody," said the agent, "this is your home station and you are to drive from here to the home station at Plum Creek. Do you know this part of the trail?"

"I should," laughed Bill. "Plum Creek is near the place where I killed my first Indian. I have traveled over the trail many times."

"Good! Then there is nothing I need to tell you except that you change horses at two stations on your way. Holladay is running his stagecoach lines as Majors ran the Pony. He is using many of the old Pony stations. The home stations are still called home stations, but the relay stations where the horses are changed are called swing stations by the drivers."

"I heard that Wild Bill Hickok is driving for Holladay. Do you know where he is?"

"Yes, he is on the Sweetwater division. Slade is still in charge of that division. You rode the Pony for him, didn't you?"

"Yes, and some day I hope to drive a stagecoach for Slade."

The agent laughed. "Well, you better get ready to drive for me. Here comes the stagecoach from the east."

"Yip! Yip! Yipee!" the warning call of the driver of the stagecoach rang out down the trail.

Several men from the stables ran toward the station.

The stagecoach with its six horses at full gallop came rattling past the fort. The driver reined in his horses and stopped the coach in front of the station.

The guard, who rode beside the driver, jumped to the ground. He opened the door of the coach. Ten passengers alighted. They followed the agent and the guard to the eating station for a home-cooked meal before continuing their journey.

"Hello, Bill," called the driver as he tossed the reins of his horses to a helper who stood waiting by the coach. "Are you driving on this division?"

"Yes," answered Bill. "I am on the stretch to Plum Creek."

"I am glad to hear it," said the driver as he sprang to the ground. He pointed with his long whip to the high seat on the stagecoach. "When you have ridden on that box for a while you will never go back to a wagon train."

"I know that you stage drivers think that your life is full of excitement, but I have had my share of adventures with the wagon trains."

"You'll change your mind," grinned the driver. "I tell you, Bill, we aren't called the knights of the reins because we lead a quiet life. I wouldn't give up my job for anything in the world."

While Bill and the driver talked, the men from the stables unhitched the horses and took them to their stalls. They returned with six fresh horses and hitched them to the stagecoach. When the passengers had finished their meal, they took their places in the coach. The guard, carrying his rifle, mounted to his seat on the box.

Bill, whip in hand, took his place on the box. Bill held the butt of his whip in his right hand. At the end of the long, hickory stock was a twelve-foot lash of buckskin.

"Give him the reins," ordered the agent.

A man handed Bill the reins for the six horses. Bill arranged the reins between the fingers of his left hand.

"Ready?" asked the agent.

Bill nodded.

"Stand back," the agent called to the two men who were holding the lead horses.

Bill lifted his whip and snapped it in the air over the heads of the horses. The horses lunged forward on the run. Bill kept his horses at a steady gallop which took the coach rapidly over the rough trail.

Bill enjoyed driving the stagecoach between Fort Kearney and Plum Creek. On each trip he was as alert and watchful for Indians and outlaws as when he rode the Pony. He took his passengers through safely and on time. Neither rough roads nor bad weather made him break his schedule.

Late one rainy night, Bill brought his stagecoach to a stop in front of the station at Plum Creek. The passengers complained to the agent that they had had a rough, hard trip.

"There is no need for a driver to hit all the bumps and holes on the trail," said one of the passengers in a loud voice. "That driver today is as bad as the others. He isn't a driver. He's a crazy man."

The agent motioned to Bill. "Come here," he called.

As Bill joined the group the agent said, "Your passengers are complaining about the rough trip they had with you."

"I know," Bill laughed, "I couldn't help over-hearing what they said." He turned to the passengers. "I am sorry," he began, "but there are good reasons why I don't try to avoid the bumps and ruts in the trail. I let my horses travel with as little guidance as possible. If I were to guide them constantly I would lose speed. However, the more important reason is that I do not want to endanger the safety of my passengers."

"I do not understand," snapped one of the passengers.

"Well, tonight for instance, the darkness and the rain made it impossible to see the trail. If my horses had learned to depend upon me, I'm afraid that we would still be far from this station. But because I allow my horses to follow the road from habit, we are here safe and sound. I have never known it to fail that when a man depends upon good horses he will get through. Do you remember when I stopped the coach and went ahead on foot?"

The passengers nodded.

"Well, that was because we were near a narrow ravine which, even in daylight, it is difficult to get through. I crawled along on my hands and knees to make sure that the rain had not washed away the trail. The ruts were deep and easy to follow and I knew my horses could make it without any help from me."

"I didn't know that we were in danger," said a passenger as Bill walked away.

"Every trip is dangerous," broke in the agent. "But with good horses and a good driver on the box there is less danger."

"Who was our driver?" asked a passenger.

"Bill Cody."

"Bill Cody!" exclaimed the passengers looking

at one another. "No wonder we made it on time in spite of the storm and darkness."

It was several hours later when the stagecoach from the west arrived at Plum Creek. It was still raining. Bill was ready to take the coach on to the station at Fort Kearney. As fresh horses were being hitched to the coach, the driver pointed to the rear of the coach where the express packages and mail were carried. This space was known as the boot.

"Gold?" asked Bill in a low voice.

The driver nodded.

"How many passengers?"

"Two rough-looking men," the driver answered.

"Thanks for the tip-off," said Bill. He climbed up to the box and took the reins as they were handed to him. The guard was already in his place beside Bill. Bill cracked the long whip and the horses started on a run down the trail.

At dawn the rain stopped. The sun came up over the horizon like a huge red ball of fire. With the coming of daylight, Bill urged his horses to greater speed. He, like the other stagecoach drivers, seldom spoke while on the box. The sounds of galloping horses, the squeaking of the leather harness, and the rattle of the coach were like music to his ears. He kept his eyes on the trail and watched the horses.

Suddenly, but without taking his eyes off the road, Bill asked his guard, "See anything over there to the right?"

"Nothing but the sagebrush on the hill," answered the guard. "Did you see something?"

"An Indian war bonnet."

"That means trouble."

"Plenty of it." Bill cracked his long whip over the heads of the horses.

The horses broke into a swift gallop. The coach bounced up and down and lurched from side to side. One minute it was on two wheels and the next minute all four wheels seemed to leave the ground. The passengers were tossed from side to side.

A war whoop rang out on the morning air. Fifty Indians sprang from their hiding places on the top of the hill. They were in full war paint and were mounted on swift ponies.

Shouting and yelling the Indians raced madly after the stagecoach.

Bill leaned forward in the box as he urged the horses over the trail. "If we make the ravine across the creek I think we can hold the Indians," he said.

"What if they beat us to it?" asked the guard.

"We lose."

The race for the ravine was a matter of life or death to those on the stagecoach. Bill, calm and steady, was slightly in the lead. But the yelling Indians were gaining ground, and arrows were beginning to whiz by. Bill, by expert driving, got to the creek first.

"Hold on!" ordered Bill as the horses plunged into the water, "I'll take care of the Indians. You watch the passengers. I don't trust them."

Bill cracked his whip and the horses dashed through the water and up the bank on the opposite side. The ravine was just ahead. They had won the race; but could Bill hold the Indians?

Bill reined in his horses as his right foot jammed down on the brake. The coach came to a sudden stop. Bill, rifle in hand, jumped to the ground. In a flash the guard was beside him. The two passengers opened the door of the coach.

"Stay where you are," ordered the guard.

"No," said the men, "we are in this fight with you."

The guard hesitated.

"All right," said Bill, "get out and fight."

Bill took careful aim with his rifle and fired. The Indian chief leading his braves threw up his hands, rolled from his pony, and fell into the water with a splash. The guard and the two men fired and three more Indians fell into the water.

The Indians in the lead tried to turn their ponies

about, but the braves in the rear kept crowding them forward into the water. Meanwhile the white men in the ravine kept up a deadly fire. The Indians soon saw that they could not continue to face the deadly fire of Bill and his companions. They turned their ponies and retreated to a safe distance.

"Get back into the coach," ordered Bill. "We must get out of here before the Indians have time to reorganize and attack us again."

The stagecoach had gone but a short distance when the guard shouted, "Here they come!"

"Give them all you have," Bill called. "Our only chance is to make the next station before they overtake us."

The wild ride continued. The Indians, slowly gaining, came closer and closer. But soon the outline of the station appeared far ahead on the trail.

"Keep firing," shouted Bill. "If the men at the station hear the shots they will ride out to help us."

Within a few minutes five mounted men from the station came racing toward them. The Indians let fly one final shower of arrows, then turned their ponies and streaked off across the plains.

The stagecoach rattled on to the swing station. The men of the station laughed and talked with Bill while the horses were being changed.

"Want us to ride on with you?" asked the agent.

"No, thank you," answered Bill, "we can make it."

At Fort Kearney the driver was waiting to take the coach on over the eastern division. Bill told the driver about the gold in the boot. He also warned him to watch the two passengers.

"They helped us in the fight with the Indians," interrupted the guard. "Why are you suspicious of them?"

"I don't know exactly," answered Bill, "but I should not like to have them as passengers in my coach without a guard."

Bill Plays a Lone Hand

BILL ENJOYED the life of a stagecoach driver. It was filled with everything he liked—action, danger, good horses, and a definite share in helping to build the West. It was a job that demanded steady nerves, quick thinking, and reckless courage.

Bill's horses soon learned to know him. When he strode from the station to mount the box they would often whinny and show eagerness to start the run. They recognized his firm but light hold on the reins and the signals of his long whip.

He took great pride in his horses. Although he expected speed and instant obedience from them he was always kind to the spirited animals. He drove them with little effort and brought the horses to the end of the run in good condition. He never used the long whip to strike a horse. He used it only as a signal to let his teams know what he wanted them to do.

187

One day after Bill had been on the run from Fort Kearney to Plum Creek for several months, the division boss said to him, "Alf Slade is in trouble again. The Indians and outlaws have attacked his stagecoaches so often that many of his drivers have quit. He has sent out a call for volunteers to take their places. I was ordered to give this message to my drivers, but I hesitated to tell you."

"Why?" questioned Bill.

"Well," answered the division boss, "I would like to have you stay on my division. I need good drivers, too. However, I know that you will volunteer to drive for Slade."

"You're right," replied Bill. "I would like to help Slade. When do I report to him?"

"As soon as you can get to Three Crossings."

"What will we do about my run today?"

"Don't worry about that," answered the division boss. "I was so certain that you would volunteer to drive for Slade that I have already given your run to another driver. Good-by and good luck."

A few days later Bill arrived at the Three Crossings home station. Slade was there.

"Hello, Bill. I'm glad but I'm not surprised to see you," said Slade. "I knew you would volunteer to drive for me. In fact, I was so sure of it that I have already decided which run you will make."

"I don't get it," laughed Bill. "The division boss at Fort Kearney gave my run to another driver before he even told me about your call for volunteers. And now, here you are with a run ready for me even before I report to you."

Slade laughed, but suddenly he became serious. "I was going to put you back on the same trail you rode for the Pony, but I have a good driver on that run. Your run will be from Three Crossings to the next home station west of here. I don't need to tell you that it is a dangerous run."

Bill nodded. "Yes, I know," he replied. "I carried the mail over that trail once for my old friend Bob."

"It's even more dangerous now," said Slade. "Your run is over the toughest part of my division. You have always wanted excitement. Well, I think you will find that the Sweetwater division can still give you plenty of action."

And on Bill's new run there was plenty of action. Indians often raced down the sand hills and attacked his stagecoach. One day his guard was killed, but Bill managed to drive on to the next station, saving the mail and the lives of his passengers. Outlaws made bold attempts to hold up his stagecoach. Winter blizzards swept the plains, but Bill made each trip safely over the snow-covered trails. Nothing could stop him! But it was on this new run that Bill's courage and his ability to think and to act quickly were put to a real test.

One day the driver from the west was late in reaching the home station where Bill was waiting to drive the stagecoach to Three Crossings. Finally the stagecoach arrived and the driver reported. "We ran into a little trouble, Bill. My guard is inside the coach. He's badly wounded."

The driver opened the door of the coach and the guard stepped out. He wore a bloody bandage around his right arm.

"Sorry about your accident," said Bill to the guard. Then turning to the driver he asked, "How many passengers are you carrying?"

"Only two, both men. But you are carrying gold on this trip, Bill."

As fresh horses were being hitched to the coach Bill examined the boot. He stopped for a moment outside the door of the coach and looked inside. The same two suspicious-looking men! He turned away with a frown on his face.

"I'll need a guard with me on this trip," he said in a low voice to the station agent.

"I wish I had one for you, Bill," replied the agent, "but I haven't a man that I can send with you. You'll either have to go alone, or wait here until a guard can be taken from some other coach."

"My coach goes through on schedule," said Bill.

Before Bill left the station he inspected his rifle and revolvers. He made sure that he had plenty of ammunition. Then he went to the stables and selected two lengths of rope which he placed under the driver's seat.

Bill climbed up on the box and, without a word, cracked his whip over the heads of his horses. He drove as fast as his horses could go over the rough trail.

After he had driven a short distance, he pulled his horses to a stop. "Here is where I get my men," he said to himself, "or they get me."

He jumped down from the driver's seat holding the two lengths of rope in his hand. He pretended to inspect one of the wheels on the coach.

Suddenly from behind him came the question, "Something wrong?"

Bill swung around holding a gun in each hand. The man was so surprised that he had no time to draw his own guns. Bill stepped forward and took the guns from the man's holster.

The other passenger called from inside the coach, "What's the delay, Cal?"

"Don't say a word or I'll let you have it," whispered Bill.

Cal, a tall, thin man, had his hands up over his head and he did not answer. Bill motioned for him to turn around. In a second he had the man's hands tied behind his back. Then Bill moved to the coach door.

"Hands up and keep 'em up," ordered Bill, opening the door. "I'll take your guns."

"What's going on?" demanded the man as he stepped to the ground, with his hands held high.

"Never mind," snapped Bill, "just turn around." When Bill had the second man securely tied he made both men climb back into the coach. He placed their guns in the space under the driver's seat.

"You won't get away with this," shouted one of the men.

"You'll get yours," snarled the other man.

Bill jumped to his seat and turned the horses around and raced back to the station. There he turned his passengers over to the surprised station agent.

"What have they done?" asked the agent.

"Nothing yet," answered Bill, "but I have a hunch that some pals of theirs are going to try something. I am making sure that these fellows won't be there to see the fun. You hold them here until you get your orders. Better lock them up and keep a sharp lookout for their pals. They may come this way, and you better be ready for them."

"We'll be ready," said the station agent.

Bill removed the gold from the boot and hid it under the cushions inside the coach. He turned the horses around and started again for Three Crossings. He drove hard in order to make up the lost time.

When he had driven a few miles beyond the place where he had bound his passengers, he came to a small hill. Three men on horseback were waiting a short distance down the trail.

As Bill neared the men, one of them held up his hand while the other two covered Bill with their rifles. Bill slammed on the brakes and reined in the horses.

"Get down!" ordered one of the men.

"You're too late," replied Bill without moving.

"What do you mean?" snarled one of the bandits.

"Your pals beat you to it," answered Bill.

"You mean they got away with the gold?"

"Search the coach," said Bill.

The three bandits hurried to the rear of the coach and opened the boot. Then they opened the door of the coach and looked inside.

"Gone!" exclaimed one of the bandits.

"Were they on foot?" asked the leader.

"They were on foot the last I saw of them," answered Bill.

"Which way did they go?" asked the leader.

"West," answered Bill.

"Come on. Let's go," said the leader. "Nobody can double-cross us and get away with it."

Bill watched the bandits ride away toward the west. "Go hunt for your pals," he said. "That will keep you busy for a couple of days. In the meantime I'll see that a posse gets on your trail."

He kicked off the brake, spoke to the horses, and drove on. The gold was safe.

That night Bill drove into Three Crossings on time. He reported to Slade how he had outwitted the outlaws by capturing two of them and sending the other three on a wild-goose chase.

"Mr. Slade," he added, "I believe a small posse of men can capture those three bandits. They will be hunting for their pals in the foothills when they ought to be hiding out a long way from this trail."

"Good work, Bill!" said Slade. "Hickok is due here in the morning. He is bringing several extra guards for this division. He would like nothing better than to round up these outlaws. That would put an end to the trouble we have been having on this division."

Early the next morning Hickok and the guards arrived. When Bill had told his story, Hickok said, "Bill, you did a fine job. You made prisoners of two outlaws and tricked the other three into hanging around until we could get on their trail."

Within an hour, Hickok and his guards, mounted on fresh horses, were ready to leave.

As Hickok bid good-by to Bill and Slade he said, "This job will not take long. Thanks to your planning, Bill, it should be easy to locate the trail of these three bandits. We'll run them down in no time."

A few days later, Slade received word from Hickok that the outlaws had been captured and that all five of the bandits were on their way to stand trial for their crimes.

Slade sent for Bill.

"Well," said Slade when Bill reported to him, "there will be no more trouble from outlaws on this division for a while. I am riding to Julesburg to start some cleaning up down there. Want to come along and help me?"

"I volunteered to make this run until you had cleaned out the bandits on this division," answered Bill. "Now, I have a little job of my own that I want to attend to."

"What do you mean?"

"I am going to get married."

In the morning, Bill was on his way eastward. It was his first trip as a passenger inside a stagecoach. As the coach rattled over the trail, he and the other passengers were tossed from side to side.

"No wonder the passengers complain about the rough, hard trips," grinned Bill to himself. "Give me the box. There is the place to ride."

Bill leaned back against the cushions and tried to make himself comfortable. In spite of the jolts and bumps he was happy. He was on his way to St. Louis and Louisa.

Champion Hunter of the Plains

ON MARCH 6, 1866, Louisa and Bill were married. The ceremony was performed before an altar of flowers in the Frederici home in St. Louis.

Louisa was a lovely bride. She wore a long white satin gown, and a bridal veil which covered her black curly hair. She was slim and dainty and her eyes shone with happiness.

Bill, dressed in a dark suit, stood beside Louisa as they greeted their friends. He was very nervous and ill at ease, but he was a handsome groom. Now and then he tossed his long yellow hair back across his shoulders.

"I would almost rather meet Black Marlin and his gang again than have to meet all these people," he laughed to himself. Then he turned and looked down at his bride and changed his mind. He smiled into her upturned face.

Louisa and Bill's first home was in Leavenworth.

198

It was a little cottage near the outskirts of the city. They were very happy.

One day Louisa was alone in the house. She was singing as she worked.

"Louisa," came Bill's voice from outdoors.

Louisa ran to the door and down to the gate where Bill, mounted on a buckskin-colored horse, was waiting.

"How do you like my new horse?" he asked. "His name is Brigham."

"Bill Cody!" exclaimed Louisa. "You didn't buy that horse! Why he is the homeliest horse I ever saw."

"I bought him to ride on my new job."

"I can't imagine what kind of job would make you buy a horse like Brigham."

"Louisa," laughed Bill, "that is no way to talk about the best buffalo horse in the West. I'll admit that Brigham is not good-looking. But I don't think the buffalo will notice his lack of good looks." He slipped from the saddle and tied Brigham to a post by the gate.

"What do you mean?" asked Louisa as she and

Bill, hand in hand, walked slowly back to the house.

"I am going to work for the company that is building the railroad," answered Bill. "My job will be to furnish enough buffalo meat each day to feed twelve hundred men working on the railroad. My pay will be five hundred dollars a month."

"That is a lot of money, but do you want to become a buffalo hunter?" asked Louisa. "You told me that you wanted to scout or to drive a stage-coach."

"Yes, I know," replied Bill. "I was offered a job as scout, and Holladay offered to give me my old stagecoach run. But the railroad is the newest development in the West and I feel that I should do my share in helping to build it."

"Bill," said Louisa, "I know that this job will take you away from home for many months. I will try to be brave. If I am not, please understand that it is because everything here in the West is new to me. But in time," she laughed a little, "I will get used to your leaving me to go off fighting Indians, hunting buffalo, or driving a stagecoach."

Louisa turned away quickly to hide the tears in

her eyes. "When do you leave?" she asked bravely.

"In the morning."

The next morning, Bill mounted Brigham and rode away. Louisa stood by the gate and waved good-by to him. The horse and rider soon disappeared from view. Louisa walked slowly back to the cottage. Long and lonely days were ahead for Bill's young bride.

Bill's job took him to the railroad camp in western Kansas. The camp was a busy place. Hundreds of men and animals were working on the roadbed of the railroad. Toward the west the endless miles of prairie stretched on to the horizon. But toward the east stretched two long rows of steel rails that had been laid by the workers. And each day the men pushed on to the west, laying the rails which were to cross a continent.

By the time the railroad camp had reached western Kansas, the laying of the track had become difficult and dangerous. It became more dangerous each day as the workers moved deeper into Indian territory.

The Indians of the plains fiercely resisted the

building of the railroad through their hunting grounds. They were afraid that the buffalo herds would be driven away or killed off by the white man. Indian braves made frequent attacks upon the workers and killed many of them. United States soldiers were finally ordered to the camp to protect the men and to guard the railroad tracks.

At first, the moving of the supplies needed for the vast undertaking had been fairly easy. But as the railroad camp moved farther and farther westward, the job became more and more difficult. The most serious problem was the supplying of fresh meat for twelve hundred men. As there was no refrigeration, it was not possible to bring fresh meat over long distances or to keep a supply in camp for the hungry men.

To solve this problem, men were hired to hunt buffalo and to deliver each day the meat needed for the men of the camp. Much of the time, however, these hunters did not bring in enough meat for the day and sometimes they ran into Indians and returned to camp without any meat. These hunters had found it very difficult to locate a buffalo herd and at the same time be on the alert against Indian attacks.

The men in charge of building the railroad soon realized that hunting buffalo was a job for a man who was not only a good hunter, but who was also a scout and an Indian fighter. Bill Cody was a good hunter, and he was a scout and Indian fighter. But could he hunt buffalo, scout, and fight Indians all at the same time? The railroad builders believed that he could, and so did Bill.

Bill reported to the man in charge of the food supply for the camp. "Cody," said the man, "I hope you have better luck than the other men who have hunted for me."

"It takes more than luck to find a herd of buffalo," laughed Bill. "How many buffalo do you need each day to feed your men?"

"Ten or twelve."

"That's a big order," said Bill.

"Don't you think you can do it?" asked the man.

"Wait and see," grinned Bill.

"All right," said the man, "I'll have the men who go out with the hunter ready with their wagons in the morning. They will butcher the buffalo you kill and bring the meat back to camp. By the way, have you seen the new gun which the government shipped out here to the soldiers? It's a breech-loading rifle. It takes a little longer to reload, but its cartridges carry more powder and a heavier bullet than the older guns."

"No, I haven't seen it," answered Bill. "It sounds like just the gun I need. Can I buy one?"

"Yes, I'll see that you get one. Is there anything else that you will need?"

"Well, I will need an extra horse to ride when I go out to find a herd."

"You mean you need a horse," laughed the man. "That horse of yours is certainly not the kind of horse you need for this job."

Bill laughed, too, but said nothing.

"I'll have an extra horse for you," continued the man, "and I'll supply you with anything else you need. But I want the meat from twelve buffalo each day."

The next morning, Bill left camp on his first buffalo hunt for the railroad. He was riding the extra horse and Brigham was being led by one of the men in the wagons.

When they were several miles from camp, Bill turned in his saddle and called to the men. "I'll ride on and if I spot a herd I'll come back for Brigham. You wait here." He gave his horse the spurs and galloped on ahead.

A short time later he came to a hill. He rode straight to the top and reined in his horse. He shaded his eyes from the bright sunlight. Far to the north he saw a large herd of buffalo peacefully grazing on the short buffalo grass of the plains.

"There they are," he said to himself as he turned his horse about and started back to the wagons.

Brigham, standing beside one of the wagons, whinnied and began to move about as Bill came near.

"Have you found a herd already?" asked the men.

"Yes, and it's a big one," answered Bill, swinging from his saddle. "We'll get our twelve buffalo and be back in camp early today."

He picked up his new rifle from one of the

wagons and loaded it. He opened his ammunition kit and filled the pockets of his buckskin shirt with cartridges. He told the men how to follow his trail with the wagons.

"Come, Brigham," he said, mounting the fresh and eager horse, "let's get some buffalo."

Brigham raced like a streak of lightning toward the herd. His long legs covered the ground in smooth, even strides.

Bill approached the herd from the rear. Without guidance Brigham galloped around to the right of the herd. As soon as he was even with them he closed in on the first buffalo. The buffalo started to run. Brigham raced along beside him.

Bill raised his gun and fired straight down behind the left shoulder of the animal. The buffalo dropped to the ground with a bullet through his heart.

At the crack of the rifle, Bill exclaimed, "What a gun! It kicks like a mule. But it certainly is a killer," he added, rubbing his shoulder. Then a smile flashed across his face. "Lucretia Borgia killed a few people in her day. I think I'll name my new gun after her."

The instant the buffalo had dropped to the ground, Brigham had dashed forward to the next animal. Bill was ready. Again the gun cracked and the second buffalo fell dead. "Lucretia Borgia, the killer, had nothing on this gun," grinned Bill. "What a rifle!"

Brigham raced alongside the third buffalo. Bill fired but the animal did not fall. Quickly he reloaded his gun and fired again. The buffalo crashed to the ground and lay still.

Brigham raced forward to another buffalo. Each time he allowed Bill only two shots for an animal.

When twelve buffalo had been killed, Bill rode back to the men in the wagons who had driven up and were watching the hunt. "There you are, boys," laughed Bill.

"I have seen many hunters," said one of the men, "but I have never seen anyone hunt as you do. Why do you get the herd running in a circle instead of letting them run across the plains?"

"It makes it easier for you," answered Bill. "If I followed the herd in a straight line, you would have to go several miles across the plains before you reached the last dead buffalo. But this way, they fall close together and you save time in butchering them."

Early that afternoon they returned to camp. The workers on the railroad were surprised to see them back so soon with the wagons loaded with fresh meat.

"Cody is a champion buffalo hunter," said one of the butchers.

"Maybe he was lucky today," said one of the

workers, "we'll wait a few days before we agree with you that he is a champion."

Early each morning, Bill and the butchers left camp. Bill always rode the extra horse so that Brigham would not be tired when he was needed to run down the buffalo. Brigham always followed with the wagons. Nearly every day, they returned to camp early in the afternoon. Sometimes, however, the buffalo roamed far from the nearby trails and it took longer to find a herd. But Bill always returned to camp with the wagons loaded with meat.

Bill was always alert and on the lookout for Indians. Several times he and his little party were attacked. But each time Bill's quick thinking and his deadly skill in firing "Lucretia Borgia" saved them from certain death.

The Indians soon learned that the new buffalo hunter with the long yellow hair and the deadly gun was to be avoided rather than attacked. They often saw him racing his buckskin horse, Brigham, after the buffalo, and watched him shoot the leaders of the circling herd. And although they hated the white man for shooting their buffalo, they could not help but admire this hunter's skill and cool courage.

The men in camp praised Bill. But Bill was quick to give the credit to his faithful horse, Brigham, and to his gun, "Lucretia Borgia."

One night, the men were gathered around a big campfire, laughing and talking.

"Bill," said one man, "you are the greatest buffalo hunter on the plains."

"Your name should be Buffalo Bill," added another man. "What about it, men? Am I right?"

"You're right," shouted the men. "Buffalo Bill!"

"Thanks, men," smiled Bill. "I can think of no finer reward than to have earned the title of Buffalo Bill."

War Drums on the Plains

BUFFALO BILL'S fame spread across the plains and throughout the entire nation. Newspapers carried long stories about his daring courage and exciting adventures. Everyone thrilled to the deeds of Buffalo Bill. He was the young hero of a sturdy, growing nation.

In the West, wherever the men of the wagon trains gathered around their campfires at night, they boasted of Buffalo Bill and claimed him as their own. Trappers and old hunters who met in trading posts exchanged stories of the youthful Buffalo Bill. They, too, claimed him as their own. Keen-eyed scouts and dashing stagecoach drivers praised him for his knowledge and skill. He was one of them. Buffalo Bill belonged to all of them. His was the spirit of the old and the new West!

In the railroad camp, Buffalo Bill was the idol of the soldiers and men. And here, one day when he returned from the day's hunt, he was called to the headquarters of the commanding officer of the troops.

"Buffalo Bill," said the officer, "an old friend of yours arrived in camp this afternoon. He is waiting to see you in my office."

"Thank you."

As Bill entered the room, a man standing by the window turned and came forward. "Billy Cody," he smiled.

"Mr. Carson!" exclaimed Bill.

"I should call you Buffalo Bill now," said Kit as they shook hands. "But I will always think of you as Billy Cody."

"Mr. Carson, you may call me anything you wish," laughed Bill. "However, I hope the men in camp don't hear you call me Billy."

Kit and Bill were together for several hours. They talked of their first meeting at old Fort Laramie and of their many experiences on the plains. Kit asked endless questions which only a good scout with a thorough knowledge of the plains could answer. He especially wanted to know about the troubles the railroad builders were having with the Indians. Bill was able to give him full information on this as well as other news of the plains. Kit was pleased.

"Billy," he said at last, "I am on my way home from Washington where I was called to meet the President. He wanted to discuss with me how we could avoid another Indian uprising. The President and his Cabinet believe that it can be avoided. But I know it cannot. I told them that a serious Indian war is about to break out on the plains."

"You are right," agreed Bill. "The Indians are preparing to go on the warpath. They are getting more hostile every day."

"And when they are ready, their war drums will be heard all over the plains," said Kit. "It will not be easy to defeat them. The mighty Sioux nation is uniting. The Sioux are born warriors and their chiefs are powerful. Sitting Bull is one of their ablest leaders. He hates the white man and he is to be feared. The Cheyennes, too, have long hated the white men. Their chief, Yellow Hand, is a fierce warrior. Do you remember him?"

"I certainly do," answered Bill. "I have never forgotten how you made him return my horse, Prince, with the other horses he had stolen."

"I don't imagine he has forgotten it either," laughed Kit. "He is a bitter enemy, but we must admit that he is an able chief.

"I have always been a friend of the Indians," continued Kit. "Many of them call me Father Kit. I know how dearly they love their tribal lands, and I understand their bitter feeling against the white men who would take those lands away from them."

"Do you think the white man could have avoided the hatred of the Indians?" asked Bill.

"Maybe we could have been friends," answered Kit, "but I don't think so. We whites belong to another civilization. We are builders. The Indians are content to live as they have always lived. They have tried time and again to stop our march of progress, but they cannot do it. This uprising will be put down, but that will not end the trouble with the Indians. There will be other uprisings later. But the day will come when the Indians and the white men will live in peace. Then we will all be Americans."

"Do you really believe that the whites and Indians can ever live together in peace?"

"Yes, I do," answered Kit, "and you will live to see it happen. I will not. My life is almost over. But I know it will happen because I know the men of the West. You are one of those men, and you are helping build a new West. I am very proud of you—Buffalo Bill."

Bill was silent.

On the plains he had earned the respect of the men with whom he worked. He had accepted their praise lightly. He had laughed and joked with them. But now as Kit Carson praised him, Bill was truly proud. He had a right to be proud. He had won the praise of the greatest of all scouts of the West.

He looked for a minute into Kit's clear, blue eyes. "Thank you, sir," he said. "For you to include me as one of the builders of the West is the highest praise I will ever receive."

The next day, Kit started his journey homeward.

Bill watched him leave the railroad camp and ride away with an escort of soldiers. When the little party disappeared, Bill made ready to go out on his daily buffalo hunt.

Week after week, trouble on the plains increased. Indians swept down upon lonely cabins and scalped men, women, and children. They attacked wagon trains and destroyed the supplies being hauled to the western forts. They burned stagecoach stations, killed the drivers and agents, and stole the horses. They made many swift attacks upon the railroad workers, killing many of them and often tearing up the rails.

The war drums had sounded. The war was on!

In May, 1868, the work of the railroad was halted. Bill rode back to Fort Hays in western Kansas. He volunteered to serve as a scout in the United States Army and he was at once accepted.

"Cody," said the commanding officer, "it seems strange that you should arrive here today. I have just learned of the death of a great scout. Kit Carson is dead."

"I am very sorry to hear this sad news," said

Bill quickly. "Kit Carson was my friend. What he did for the West will never be forgotten."

"Carry on for him, Cody."

"I shall try to do that, sir."

Bill had enjoyed his work with the railroad men, but now he was back in the work that he loved best. He needed a swift, wiry horse for his long rides as an army scout. He left Brigham with a friend and selected one of the best of the government horses for his new mount. "Lucretia Borgia," his heavy buffalo gun, was put away. Bill chose a lighter rifle to use in its stead so as not to give his horse any unnecessary weight to carry.

For the next several months, Bill scouted for the army and carried messages from one fort to another in the hostile Indian territory. He had many narrow escapes from the Indians. While other scouts often failed to get through, Bill Cody made his rides safely.

During the summer, the Indians made many swift surprise attacks and then as swiftly disappeared. The soldiers were kept constantly on the move. However, they were unable to put an end to these sudden raids. Then, with the coming of winter, the Indians left the warpath and went to their winter homes.

The commanding general called a war council of his officers and scouts. He decided on a bold plan.

"We will follow the Indians to their faraway camps," said the general. "We will attack their villages one after the other."

"General, it is impossible to fight on the plains during the winter," protested an officer. "Our men cannot face the blizzards, nor can supplies be brought to us over snow-covered trails. We must wait until spring."

Many of the officers agreed that it would be impossible to carry out the general's plan.

"What do you think about it, Cody?" asked the general. "You know the plains. Can our army carry the war to the enemy during the winter months?"

"I believe that it can, sir," answered Bill. "The Indians would be taken by surprise. Even if we take only a few of their villages, we will be carrying on an offensive war against them. So far they have been fighting when and where they chose to fight. We must gain the advantages of surprise attacks and of choosing when and where we shall fight."

"The army marches!" The general brought his fist down on his desk. "Get ready for action at once. We leave at dawn tomorrow."

As Bill left the meeting, an officer followed him. He was a dashing, handsome, young man. His quick smile and kindly manner made friends for him wherever he went.

"Cody," he said, "I am George A. Custer, in command of the Seventh Cavalry. I am going to ask the general to make you my chief of scouts. The Seventh needs a scout like you."

"Thank you," replied Bill. "But I have already been assigned as chief of scouts to the Fifth Cavalry."

"Just my luck," laughed Custer. "Well, maybe some other time you can scout for me."

"Whenever the Fifth doesn't need me," smiled Bill, "I'll come to you for a job."

"Good. Remember that."

At dawn the army took the trail toward the winter villages of the Indians. Blizzards swept across the plains. Men, horses, and mules struggled over snow-covered plains. Many of the animals were unable to stand the bitter cold. They broke under the strain of the struggle and fell on the trail. Wagons, loaded with supplies, had to be left in snowbanks.

But the army marched on!

The Indians were taken by surprise. Village after village was destroyed. The campaign was a success. When the power of the Indians was completely broken, they begged for peace.

"Come to nearest fort," the commanding general said to the chiefs. "We make treaty."

A few weeks later, the peace treaty was signed. The Indian chiefs were ready to leave the fort to return to their tribes.

Bill, standing near the heavy wooden gates of the fort with a group of scouts, watched the chiefs leave the meeting. One chief stopped for a moment, looked at him, and then walked on.

"Red Hawk!" exclaimed Bill. He went after the

chief. "Red Hawk," he called in a loud voice.

The chief turned and, holding his bright red blanket closely about him, waited motionless.

"Red Hawk, don't you know me?"

"I do. You are Pa-ha-ska."

"Pa-ha-ska?" questioned Bill.

"Yes, your Indian name, 'Long, yellow hair.' You are my enemy."

"We were friends when we were at Fort Laramie."

"That was years ago. Now I am chief of my people. I am Rain-in-the-Face. I took my father's name. He hated the white men. I know now why he hated them. Once, you were my friend. Now, you are with white soldiers. You know my people. You know our habits. You know how to follow our trails. Now, you fight my braves."

"But we have signed a peace treaty. Now, we can be friends again," said Bill.

"Never! Yellow Hand is right. You are an enemy of my people. I hate you, Pa-ha-ska."

Boots and Saddles

THE PEACE treaty had been signed. The Indians were given a large tract of land in what is now the state of South Dakota. They were also given the right to hunt on the land farther west. One of the provisions of the treaty was that no white people would be allowed to enter the lands given to the Indians.

"This land is your own," the Indians were told.

The treaty put an end to the Indian war. The general and most of the officers and soldiers who had come west to fight the Indians returned to the East. However, the troops which had been stationed in the forts on the plains were ordered to remain on duty in their old posts. They were needed to guard the settlers and to see that the treaty was not broken.

The Indian war drums were silent. But the people who lived in the West knew that danger was not gone from the plains. They knew that the Indians still hated the whites and that roving bands of braves would quickly take advantage of any opportunity to steal or to kill.

As soon as the treaty was signed, the Fifth Cavalry rode northward to Fort McPherson where it had been assigned to duty. Bill Cody, chief of scouts, rode with the Fifth to his new headquarters. Bill and his scouts were to be the eyes and ears of the commanding officer. They were to keep him fully informed of what was going on in the area which the fort was protecting.

Every day, Bill and his scouts made their rides over the plains, keeping a close watch on the Indian villages and camps. The reports they brought in from these trips enabled the commanding officer to keep his soldiers ever on guard against sudden Indian attacks.

Slowly the months passed without any signs of Indian trouble. Many of the soldiers and scouts at Fort McPherson sent for their wives and children to join them at the fort. Louisa Cody and baby daughter were among the first to arrive.

For the next few years the Codys lived in a log cabin near the fort. Here in this little cabin their son was born. They named him Kit Carson Cody in honor of the great scout.

Each year, more and more white men came to the West. Many of them tried to settle on the land which had been given to the Indians. When they were told that they could not enter the Indian lands they became angry. Some of them defied the treaty and settled on the Indian reservation in spite of the warnings they received. Many of them were killed by the Indians.

The United States Government moved to put an end to the trouble between the settlers and the Indians. Soldiers were sent to the West to keep white people off the Indian reservations. The soldiers were to protect the Indians and to prevent the white people from breaking the treaty.

Some of the Indian chiefs, however, did not trust the government or the soldiers. These chiefs still hoped to unite all the Plains Indians in a war against the whites. They hoped to drive all white people from all of the lands of the West.

Bill continued to act as scout for the Fifth Cavalry. Now and then a band of braves went on the warpath. But, due to Bill's alertness, these uprisings were quickly put down by the troops.

One day, Bill and his scouts returned to the fort after a week's ride over their part of the plains. Bill went at once to the commanding officer of the fort to make his report.

"Cody," said the officer, "while you were gone, General Custer and his Seventh Cavalry were here. The Seventh is on its way to the Black Hills in the Indian reservation. Custer asked about you. He still wants you to scout for him."

Bill laughed. "I am sorry to have missed General Custer. I should like to be one of his scouts. But as long as the Fifth needs me, I shall stay with the Fifth."

"Good!" exclaimed the officer. "Now what about your trip?"

Bill frowned. "The Indians are more hostile than they have been for some time," he said. "Some of their more powerful chiefs are trying to unite all the Plains Indian tribes. If they are successful it will mean another hard-fought Indian war."

"Who are some of the chiefs trying to unite the Indians?"

"Well, among the Sioux chiefs are Rain-in-the-Face, Crazy Horse, Red Cloud, Gall, and many others. Perhaps the Indian with the greatest influence and power is old Sitting Bull. He is a great warrior and his Sioux braves are loyal to him. The Sioux are trying to get the Cheyennes to join them. Chief Yellow Hand of the Cheyennes has long hated the white men, and I am sure that he and his braves will join the Sioux if they go on the warpath."

"I am afraid that you are right, Cody. We need more troops here in the West to keep the Indians quiet. They seem to be forgetting the treaty they made with the white men."

"The white men are the ones who are breaking the treaty," interrupted Bill. "It must be stopped at once. If it is not, we cannot blame the Indians for going on the warpath this time."

"Are you defending the Indians?"

"I am sorry for them," answered Bill. "They are determined to hold what little land they can still call their own. They must be protected from the greedy settlers who are slipping into their reservation and grabbing their land. If we can't stop the land-grabbers we are in for a great deal of trouble."

"That is why the United States Government sent General Custer out here," said the officer. "He is to keep the white people out of the Indian reservation in the Black Hills."

Custer might have succeeded in protecting the lands of the Indians but for the discovery of gold in the Black Hills. The news swept across the country. Thousands of white men hurried westward to stake claims in the new gold fields. And while the white men overran the Indians' land and mined the gold in it, the Indians prepared for war.

Once again the war drums sounded over the plains. Once again the Indians were on the warpath.

Sitting Bull took the leading part in preparing for action. His braves raced their wiry ponies across the plains. They carried Sitting Bull's message to the chiefs of other tribes: "We make our

plans together. Meet me at camp on Little Big Horn. Come! Come at once!"

In the western forts the bugle call of the United States Army rang out sharp and clear. The bugle call of "Boots and Saddles" answered the slow, steady beat of Indian war drums.

The Fifth Cavalry was transferred from Fort McPherson to Fort Laramie.

As soon as the Fifth reached Fort Laramie, it

was ordered to scout the country between the fort and the Black Hills to the north.

Bill and his scouts led the way. All day, and every day, the cavalrymen were in the saddle. Several times they came upon hostile bands of Indians who promptly fled after a short skirmish.

When they had finished the scouting assigned to them, the troops started back to Fort Laramie.

One night, just before dark, the men made camp

near a small creek. Bill was eating his supper with a group of officers when one young officer said, "I joined the Fifth because I thought I was going to see some real fighting. So far we have had only a few skirmishes with small bands of roving Indians."

"Wait until you meet the Sioux and you will change your mind," said Bill.

The young officer laughed. "The Sioux! That's all I hear. Where are they? They must be staying close to their reservation since they learned that the army is on the march. They act as if they are afraid."

"Don't you believe it," answered Bill seriously. "The Sioux are our most powerful enemy. They are fearless fighters and their leaders have great military skill. Before we defeat them, you will see plenty of real fighting."

"General Custer is in the Black Hills among the Sioux. He doesn't seem to think they are so powerful. He is not afraid of them," argued the young officer.

"General Custer is one of the bravest and most

daring officers I ever knew," answered Bill. "He knows the Indians and their ways of fighting. I only hope that he doesn't underestimate the great strength of the Sioux."

The conversation was interrupted by an orderly who saluted the commanding officer and said, "Sir, a scout from the north has just arrived. He has an important message for you."

"Bring him to me," ordered the general.

In a few moments, the scout came forward.

"What is your message?" asked the general.

"Custer and a large number of his men have been massacred," answered the scout.

"Custer and his men massacred!" cried the general. "What happened? How?"

"General Custer and his six hundred men found the camp of Sitting Bull on the Little Big Horn River in Montana," began the scout. "Custer had been told by his scouts that there were only about six hundred Indians in the camp. He decided to attack the camp from three directions and divided his troops into three units of about two hundred men each. He led his unit straight against the center of the camp. He found almost six thousand Indians in the camp instead of six hundred.

"Custer and his two hundred men were so greatly outnumbered they didn't have a chance," continued the scout. "They were surrounded and every man was killed before the other two units could reach them. The battle lasted only twenty minutes."

For a moment Bill and the officers sat in stunned silence. Then they slowly pushed aside their unfinished meal.

"Men," said the general rising to his feet, "let us salute the spirit of as brave an officer as ever wore a uniform."

At dawn the Fifth Cavalry was on its way northward. All thought of returning to Fort Laramie had been dismissed. This was war, and the Fifth was on its way to claim its share of the fighting. The men of the Fifth were fired with one desire— to avenge the death of their comrades in arms. They spared neither themselves nor their horses. Day after day they rode over the plains toward the land of the Sioux.

One evening after they had made camp, the general received a message. "A thousand Cheyennes are on the warpath," it said. "They are headed for War Bonnet Creek to join Sitting Bull and his victorious braves. The Cheyennes are still fifty miles from the creek. They must not be allowed to join the Sioux. Can the Fifth stop them?"

The general sent for Bill Cody.

"Cody," he asked, "how far are we from War Bonnet Creek?"

"Eighty miles, sir."

The general shook his head. "Then we can't make it."

"What do you mean, sir?"

"A thousand Cheyenne warriors are headed for War Bonnet Creek. They are to wait there for Sitting Bull to arrive with his warriors. Their plan is to unite forces under the command of Sitting Bull.

"That must not happen," broke in Bill. "If the Sioux and Cheyennes unite, we are lost. We must stop them."

"The only way that we can stop them is to get

to the creek before the Cheyennes," said the general. "And we haven't a chance to do that."

"Why not?"

"Because they are only fifty miles from the creek while we are eighty miles away."

"General, the Fifth has never failed to carry out its orders. We can—we must make it."

"How?"

"Follow me. I know this country. I can get you there on time."

The general hesitated. "All right, Cody," he said at last, "the Fifth will follow you. But remember, if you fail to get us there in time it may cost the lives of every man in this cavalry. If you fail, another Custer massacre may take place."

Bill drew himself to his full height. "General," he said, "as a scout I give you my word that I will not fail. The Fifth will be waiting for the Cheyennes at War Bonnet Creek."

War Bonnet Creek

Two HOURS later the Fifth Cavalry had broken camp and was on its way. Bill, mounted on a white horse, was in the lead. The race for War Bonnet Creek was on!

"We can't make good time until daylight," Bill said to himself. He kept his horse at a steady trot over the trail. "But we are on our way," he added.

On through the darkness the Fifth followed its chief scout. The men rode silently. They kept their mounts at a steady pace.

At last the early morning light spread across the plains. The trail was now easy to follow. The men urged their horses to greater speed. They came to a small stream. A halt was called for a short rest and breakfast of hardtack and cold meat.

"General," said Bill, "I am going on ahead. Keep the men moving and keep them together."

"All right, Cody," replied the general with a

smile. "We will carry out your orders."

Bill rode on. He watched the trail and studied the distant rolling hills. Now and then, some far-away object attracted his attention. Each time he kept his keen eyes on the object until he was certain that it was not an Indian.

"If that were an Indian," he said to himself, "I would know it by this time. Their scouts always give themselves away by running and jumping around. But I am not going to tell them how I think they should scout," he laughed.

Several times during the day Bill rode back and reported to the general and then rode on ahead again. Late in the afternoon, he reported, "We can reach War Bonnet Creek tonight if we ride on without our supply wagons. If we travel with the wagon train we won't reach the creek until some-time tomorrow morning."

The general frowned. "We need our supplies. But we must reach War Bonnet Creek before the Cheyennes."

"Then I suggest that we leave one company of men to follow with the wagon train," said Bill.

"The rest of the cavalry must push on as rapidly as possible."

"Very well, I'll give the order. Ride on."

Late that night, the Fifth reached War Bonnet Creek. They had covered eighty miles in thirty-one hours. Camp was made, but no campfires were lighted. Guards were posted, and the weary men were soon asleep.

Before dawn, Bill left the camp. He said to a guard, "If the general asks for me, tell him that I have gone out to do a little scouting."

"Aren't you going to take your horse?"

"Not this morning," answered Bill. "This time I'll have to do some walking."

Quietly, Bill made his way to the creek. He followed the winding bank upstream for almost a mile in the direction from which the Cheyenne trail led to the creek. Every now and then, he dropped to the ground and carefully examined the earth for the telltale hoofprints of Indian ponies, or the footprints of Indian scouts. He found none.

"The Cheyennes may have used that old trick of riding upstream in the water to throw us off their trail," he said to himself. "I had better scout the opposite bank of the creek before I report to the general that we have won the race to War Bonnet."

He waded across the creek and carefully studied the ground for Indian signs. "We've made it!" he said at last. "The Cheyennes have not crossed the War Bonnet!"

He started back toward camp. "There are no signs," he said to himself, "yet something tells me that the Cheyennes are near."

He studied the land to the west and the hills to the south. Suddenly he stiffened.

"There they are!" he exclaimed. "A scouting party of about fifty Cheyenne braves. That means that the rest of the warriors can't be far away."

Bill hurried back to camp and reported to the general. The men were ordered to mount their horses and to remain hidden behind a large bluff.

"Cody," said the general, "take me to the nearest spot where I can get a look at the scouting party."

The general and several of his officers mounted their horses and followed Bill who led them to a nearby hill.

"There they are," said Bill when they reached the top of the hill. He pointed to the south.

"They don't seem aware of the fact that the Fifth Cavalry is waiting for them," laughed the general. "What a surprise we will give them!"

The Cheyenne braves, riding their wiry little ponies, were headed toward the creek. Suddenly they divided and about twenty braves raced off toward the west.

"What are they doing now, Cody?" asked an officer.

"It looks like trouble," answered Bill. He raised himself up in the stirrups of his saddle.

"I don't see anything," said the officer.

"General," questioned Bill, "did you order your company of soldiers to remain with the supply train until they joined us at War Bonnet?"

"Yes. Why do you ask?"

"The Cheyennes may have sighted the wagon train," answered Bill. "No, I was wrong. Now I see what they are doing. Two of your soldiers have left the wagon train and are riding straight into a trap."

"They were ordered to remain with the train," broke in the general. "Cody, you must be wrong."

"I'm afraid I'm right, sir."

"Then we must attack the Indians at once."

"If we do that, sir, it would warn the Cheyennes that the Fifth is waiting for them. Let me take fifteen men and make the attack. We can rescue the soldiers without letting the Indians know that the Fifth is here."

"Very well, Cody. Good luck."

Bill and fifteen scouts made the attack and rescued the soldiers. Several Indians were killed. The remaining braves turned their ponies about and raced for the hills.

"After them," shouted Bill. "Don't let them escape."

At that moment a war whoop split the air. A thousand mounted Cheyenne warriors sprang from their hiding places on the top of a hill. Another war whoop, and they dashed down the hill toward Bill and his men.

Bill brought his men to a sudden stop. "Get back to the general at once," he ordered. "Tell him to order half of his men to attack from the left and half from the right. I will try to delay the Indians until the men are in position. Hurry!"

"We won't leave you here," protested a scout. "You haven't a chance against all those Indians."

"Leave that to me. Do as I say," ordered Bill.

He gave his horse the spurs and galloped straight toward the yelling Indians.

The Indians were taken by surprise at this unexpected move. They made no attempt to follow the fifteen men who were now racing toward the woods along the creek where the Fifth was hidden. Instead they reined in their ponies and watched Bill as he rode toward them. In another minute the Indians recognized him.

"Pa-ha-ska! Pa-ha-ska!" they shouted.

Bill stopped his horse about a hundred yards from the front lines of the surprised braves. The chief of the Cheyennes called out an order. He waved his arms and his braves made a path for him to ride toward Bill.

Alone, the tall handsome chief rode forward. He was in full war paint. His buckskin trousers were

fringed and richly embroidered with bright colored beads. He wore his beautiful war bonnet of eagle feathers with dignity and pride. He was dressed as only a great chief is dressed when on the warpath.

"Pa-ha-ska!" he called. "Pa-ha-ska!"

"Yellow Hand!" exclaimed Bill.

"Come on and fight if you dare," shouted Yellow Hand. "Come on and fight alone."

"I have come," was Bill's prompt reply.

They gave their horses the spurs and raced toward each other.

"Pa-ha-ska," shouted Yellow Hand as he drew a pistol from his belt, "you big fool to fight big chief of Cheyennes."

Quick as a flash Bill's revolver barked. Yellow Hand's pony dropped. The chief was thrown to the ground. As he fell, his pistol was knocked from his hand. In an instant, however, he recovered his gun and sprang to his feet.

At that moment Bill's galloping horse stepped into a hole and fell, throwing Bill heavily to the ground. Bill jumped to his feet, but he was stunned. Yellow Hand advanced, gun in hand.

"Pa-ha-ska! I get your scalp," hissed Yellow Hand.

The angry voice of the chief was all Bill needed. He threw back his head. His long yellow hair fluttered in the breeze. He was ready!

Their revolvers flashed. Yellow Hand's shot missed, but Bill's aim found its mark. Yellow Hand staggered and fell forward dead.

Bill ran to the dead chief. He removed the war bonnet and, holding it high, shouted, "This one for Custer!"

The Cheyenne braves were spellbound. Then a war whoop rang out. They dashed toward the white man who had killed their chief.

A volley from the Fifth Cavalry stopped their wild charge. The soldiers attacking from the right and left, closed in on the Indians. The plain instantly became a scene of wild confusion as Indian ponies and their riders went down before the withering fire from the cavalry.

The Indians fought stubbornly, but the Fifth was on the warpath to avenge the death of Custer and his men. Within a few minutes, the Cheyennes were racing over the hills in disorderly retreat.

"Cody," praised the general, "your courage and your quick thinking saved the day. Our victory belongs to you."

Bill smiled, "Thank you, sir. But don't forget that I ride with the Fighting Fifth."

* * * *

The war continued, but the power of the Indians had been broken at War Bonnet Creek when the Cheyennes and the Sioux had failed to unite. The Indians fought on for many long weeks, bravely and stubbornly. They could not stop the steady advance of the soldiers. Finally, Sitting Bull, a few chiefs, and several hundred braves fled to Canada. Then, one by one, the tribes surrendered and begged for peace.

And so at last peace came to the great rolling plains and to all the West.

The End of the Trail

THE FLIGHT of Sitting Bull and his followers to Canada marked the end of real Indian wars in the West. The peace which followed was broken only by an occasional skirmish which was quickly put down. The Indians were given reservations and were required to stay on them. As Kit Carson had said, the time had come at last when the Indians and the whites were to live together in peace.

The next few years brought many changes to the West. Cities and towns sprang up where once Indian villages had stood. Fields of grain grew on the old Indian hunting grounds. Railroads carried the freight once hauled by the wagon trains. Old stagecoaches no longer rattled over the trails and only a few herds of buffalo were left from the millions of buffalo which once roamed the plains.

A new West was being built. But the restless spirit of the old West still filled Bill Cody's heart. Now that the old West was no more, what could he do?

There was no longer need for a scout, no place for a stagecoach driver, no job with a wagon train, no rides for the Kid of the Pony, and no Indians to fight. And these were the jobs that he had mastered in doing his share in the building of the West. What could he do now?

"Louisa," he said one day, "there is nothing left for me to do."

"Oh, yes there is, Bill," smiled Louisa. "You are still young. You can begin a new life—perhaps in the East."

"And leave the West? I couldn't do that, Louisa. I could never be happy away from the West."

"You need a change. Why don't we go back to St. Louis and visit my family?"

"All right," agreed Bill. "But before we go to St. Louis, we will stop off and visit my sister in Leavenworth."

A week later, the Codys arrived in Leavenworth.

Here, too, many changes had taken place. Only a few of the old landmarks still remained.

When Bill took his first walk down the old familiar streets, he came to the old warehouse which had belonged to the greatest freighting firm of the old West. The weather-beaten sign was still there. But the only words that could still be read were Gateway to the West.

"Gateway to the West," said Bill to himself. Almost as if it were yesterday, he recalled the first time he had come to ask "Uncle Alec" Majors for a job. In imagination he heard again a group of scouts laughing and talking. Nearby, wagon bosses shouted their orders. Bull whips cracked and teams of oxen strained forward in their yokes. The wagon train was off!

Bill Cody—Buffalo Bill—was reliving the old days on the plains. He recalled the long weary miles, the good fellowship of the men, the songs, the jokes, the dangers, the hardships, and the stage-coach holdups. Once again he saw the Indians hiding in ambush along the trails, the burning wagon trains, the buffalo stampedes, and outlaws lying in wait to hold up the Boys of the Pony.

A rattling stagecoach, with six galloping horses, pulled to a stop and the passengers alighted. The guard jumped down from the box. The driver, his hat tipped back on his head, threw the reins to the station agent. The knight of the reins stepped down from his high seat and strode into the station followed by a group of excited boys.

"The old West," he said to himself. "The old wild West!"

He started on down the street. Suddenly he stopped. "Why didn't I think of this before?" he asked himself. He laughed aloud. "Now I know what I can do to help both the West and the East. I'll take the West—my old wild West—to the East. I'll show the people in the East what the men of the West did to help build a nation."

Bill went to work at once. He organized a Wild West Show. The show was to be the story of the dangers and hardships faced by the pioneers in their struggle against the Indians of the plains. It was to be the story of the Winning of the West.

For his show, Bill bought old covered wagons,

stagecoaches, horses, mules, and oxen. He hired many of his old friends—old stagecoach drivers, wagon bosses, teamsters, and station agents—to act the parts they had played in real life. He hired Indians and scouts and Boys of the Pony to play the parts that gave true pictures of life in the Wild West.

Buffalo Bill's Wild West Show was a great success. For nearly thirty years Bill kept his show before the American people. With it he toured England and many European countries. Wherever he went the people came in great crowds to see his show and to cheer him. Buffalo Bill was a hero to millions of people, young and old, rich and poor.

During these years Bill Cody had changed but little. His slim figure was still proudly erect. His brown eyes were still keen and bright. His long yellow hair had turned white and he walked more slowly, but that was all. He remained a man of the old West.

Then, late in the year of 1916, Bill was taken ill. When the doctor had examined him, Bill asked, "Is this the end of the trail, Doctor?"

The doctor hesitated. He did not answer.

"Tell me. I am not afraid. If I am not going to get well I want to know it now. If I am going to die I want to go home—to the West."

"Go home, Buffalo Bill," said the doctor. "Go back to your West. You have reached the end of the trail."

* * * *

On January 10, 1917, Buffalo Bill died in Denver, Colorado. He was buried on the top of nearby Lookout Mountain. His death was mourned throughout the world.

Every year thousands of people come to the simple grave of this great scout to honor his memory.

Buffalo Bill, the last of the great scouts, is at rest in the West that he loved so well. His spirit looks out over the trails he once rode and over the plains he helped make safe for the settlers of a growing nation. He had the courage of a scout, the vision of a pioneer, and the faith of a loyal American.

Word List

adobe—ə'dōbē
ammunition—,amyə'nishən
bowie—'büē
Bridger—'brijə(r)
Brigham—'brigəm
bugle—'byügəl
buttes—'byüt
cavalry—'kavəlrē
cavayard—'kavə,yärd
Cheyenne—(')shī'an
corral—kə'ral
Frederici—fred(ə)'rēsē
hostile—'hä|stˀl
Julesburg—'jülz;bərg
Kearney—'kärnē
Leavenworth—'levən,wərth

levee—'levē
Lucretia Borgia—lü'krēshə 'bȯrjə
massacred—'masəkə(r)d
mochila—mō'chēlə
Pa-ha-ska—pə'hȧskə
papoose—pa'püs
plainsman—'plānzmən
Platte—'plat
posse—'päsē
schedule—'ske(,)j|ül
schooner—'skünə(r)
Sioux—'sü
tepee—'tē(,)pē
Utah—'yü,tȯ
whoop—'h|üp
yoke—'yōk

The system of indicating pronunciation is used by permission of the publishers of *Webster's Third New International Dictionary*, copyright 1961 by G. & C. Merriam Co., Publishers of the Merriam-Webster Dictionaries.

252